# McGRAW-HILL SCIENCE

Macmillian/McGraw-Hill Edition

## Activity Resources

**GRADE 5**

Macmillan
McGraw-Hill
New York Farmington

*Macmillan/McGraw-Hill*

*A Division of The* ***McGraw-Hill*** *Companies*



Printed in the United States of America
Activity Resources ISBN 0-02-280177-4/5
4 5 6 7 8 9 024 06 05 04 03 02

# Table of Contents

Name ______________________ Date ____________

Explore Activity

Lesson 1

# What Do Plants Have in Common?

**Materials**

- *Elodea* plant
- moss plant
- fern plant
- geranium (or other flowering plant)
- microscope
- microscope slide
- coverslip
- dropper
- water

**Hypothesize** Most plants live on land, but some live in water. Some are tiny, and others grow very large. Do all plants have common traits?

Write a **Hypothesis:**

Possible hypothesis: All plants have common traits, such as leaves, stems, and roots.

## Procedure

1. **Observe** Your group will need to get four plants from your teacher. Observe each of the plants.
2. **Communicate** As you observe each plant, draw the plant and describe it.

   Possible answer: The *Elodea,* fern, and geranium have roots, stems, and leaves. The geranium has flowers. The moss does not appear to have stems. All of the plants are green.

3. Make a wet-mount slide of an *Elodea* leaf by placing the leaf in a drop of water in the center of the slide and carefully putting a coverslip on top.
4. **Observe** View the slide under low power.

   Students may see chloroplasts moving in the cytoplasm.

5. **Communicate** Draw what you see.

Name ______________________ Date ____________

**Explore Activity**
Lesson 1

## Drawing Conclusions

1. **Communicate** What plant traits can you observe without using the microscope?

   Possible answer: The plants have differently shaped green leaves and roots. Some have stems. One plant has flowers.

2. **Communicate** What other plant traits can you observe with the microscope?

   Possible answer: Plants are made of many box-like cells that have walls and contain 6 green structures.

3. **Define** From what you observed, come up with your own definition of a plant.

   Possible answer: A plant is an organism that has green leaves, roots, and box-like cells with walls.

4. **Going Further: Hypothesize** Examine some other kinds of plants with the microscope. Do all the plants seem to have the same traits, or do some plants look quite different from the others? Do plants that look similar under the microscope have the same traits? How would you set up an experiment to find out?

   Possible answer: Under the microscope, plant cells look similar even though the plants may look very different. Plants with similar looking cells could be examined to see if they have any other traits

## Inquiry

Think of your own questions that you might like to test. What traits are common in plant cells?

My Question Is:

Possible question: What is inside plant cells?

How I Can Test It:

Closely examine cells from different plants using a microscope.

My Results Are:

Plant cells contain various structures that seem to be similiar in different plants.

Name ______________________ Date ____________

Alternative Explore

Lesson 1

# A Look at Plant Cells

## Procedure

1. Look at prepared slides of a variety of plant cells. Describe what you see. Then make a drawing of each kind of cell.

   Drawings may vary. Students may draw and describe a nucleus, cell wall, and chloroplasts.

### Materials

- prepared slides of plant cells
- various colors of clay
- toothpicks
- pieces of colored paper

2. Use clay and other materials to make a model of a plant cell. Be sure to show inside structures.

## Drawing Conclusions

1. How were the cells you looked at similar?

   They all had structures that look like walls. Depending on the slides available, students will likely say that most or all have green structures.

2. How were the cells you looked at different from each other?

   Answers will vary depending on the slides available. Students may note differences in shape—boxy versus flat.

3. How did you show different plant parts in your model?

   Answers will vary. Green clay or green colored paper should be used to represent green structures.

Name ______________________ Date ____________

QUICK LAB

FOR SCHOOL OR HOME

Lesson 1

# Tubelike Plant Parts

**Hypothesize** How does water get to different parts of a plant? Write a **Hypothesis:**

Possible hypothesis: Water travels in tubelike structures to different parts of a plant.

## Materials

- celery stalk
- bit of moss
- lettuce leaf
- oak or maple leaf
- water
- food coloring
- narrow-mouthed bottle
- hand lens
- knife

## Procedure

1. **Observe** Use a hand lens to examine the parts of a celery stalk, piece of moss, or leaf. Draw what you see.

   Drawings may show: The celery stalk has strings running through the stalk. The lettuce, celery, and oak/maple leaves have veins. The moss has a large surface area and no major stems or veins.

2. **Hypothesize** Make a guess about the function of each structure.

   Possible answer: Water travels through the stringy structures in the celery stem and veins in the leaves. Most of the leaf cells make food. The leaves absorb energy from sunlight and carbon dioxide from air. Water is absorbed directly into moss cells, which also absorb energy from sunlight and carbon dioxide from the air.

3. Add water to a bottle so the water is about an inch deep. Add a few drops of food coloring to the water.

Name ______________________ Date __________

QUICK LAB
FOR SCHOOL OR HOME
Lesson 1

4. Try putting different plant pieces in the colored water. Observe them after a few minutes. Record your observations.

Possible answer: Different plant pieces will absorb the colored water changing the color of the plant pieces.

## Drawing Conclusions

5. **Interpret Data** Write an explanation. Include a statement about why your observations support or don't support your guess.

Possible answer: The highly colored celery stalk and leaves support the idea that the primary function of the stem is to transport water into the leaves. Color in the moss indicates that the cells absorbed water directly since major stems are not visible. The colored water may have entered the lettuce and other leaves through vein openings or through pores used to absorb carbon dioxide and release water.

6. **Going Further** The tubelike structure, or vascular tissue, in a celery stem transports water very well. How can you demonstrate water moving up a tube? Write and conduct an experiment.

My Hypothesis Is:

Possible hypothesis: Capillary action helps stems to transport water.

My Experiment Is:

Possible experiment: Place the tip of a capillary tube or thin, clear plastic straw in water. Compare the height of the water inside and outside of the tube/straw.

My Results Are:

The water inside the tube is higher.

Name________________________________ Date______________

Explore Activity
Lesson 2

# How Do a Plant's Parts Help It Survive?

**Materials**

- cactus
- water plant, such as an *Elodea* or a duckweed
- flowering plant, such as a geranium

**Hypothesize** How may plants from different places differ from each other? How do the differences help the plants survive in their surroundings?

Write a **Hypothesis:**

Possible hypothesis: Plants from different places may have parts that differ in size or shape. These differences may help them survive in their surroundings.

## Procedure

1. **Observe** Look at the physical properties of the leaves of each plant. Note the color, size, and shape of the leaves.

   Possible answer: Cactus leaves are thin, sharp spines. Geraniums have broad green leaves. The Elodea has tiny green leaves.

2. **Communicate** List any other plant parts that you see.

   Possible answer: All the plants have stems. The geranium has flowers. The cactus and geranium have roots, but the Elodea does not.

3. **Communicate** Observe the physical properties of these parts and record your observations.

   Possible answer: The cactus has a very thick stem and long roots. The geranium has thin stems and short roots.

## Drawing Conclusions

1. **Interpret Data** How do the parts of a cactus help it survive in a hot, dry desert?

   Possible answer: The spines reduce water loss and protect the plant from animals. The stem makes food and can also store water.

2. **Infer** Would the geranium be able to survive in the desert? Why or why not?

   Probably not. Too much water would be lost through the large surface area of the leaves, and the thin stem would not store water.

3. **Infer** Could the water plant survive out of water? Why or why not?

   No, the water plant lacks the roots needed to live in soil.

4. **Going Further: Predict** Could these plants survive outdoors where you live? Why or why not? For each plant, what conditions would you have to change so that the plant could survive outside where you live?

   Answers depend on the precipitation and temperature conditions of your area. By providing proper temperature and water conditions, the cactus and flowering plant might survive. The water plant probably would not survive.

**Inquiry**

Think of your own questions that you might like to test. How do plants adapt to the change of seasons?

My Question Is:

Possible question: How do trees survive the change of seasons?

How I Can Find Out:

Possible answer: Write down different types of local trees. Research or recall from memory how the tree appears in different seasons.

My Results Are:

Some trees lose their leaves in the fall and grow new leaves in spring.

Name ______________________ Date ____________

Alternative Explore

Lesson 2

# Plant Parts

## Procedure

1. Observe the different stems and describe how they are different.

   Answers will vary.

2. Observe the different leaves and describe how they are different.

   Answers will vary.

3. Observe the different roots and describe how they are different.

   Answers will vary. Some roots are thick with few branching hairs. Some roots are thin and hairy.

## Materials

- stems of different lengths
- leaves of different sizes and shapes
- taproots and fibrous roots

## Drawing Conclusions

1. For each stem that you looked at, predict where the plant might live and how its stem helps the plant survive.

   Possible environments: dry, wet, hot, cold. Possible roles of stems: transport water, give support, store water, store food.

2. For each leaf that you looked at, predict where the plant might live and how its leaf helps the plant survive.

   Possible environments: dry, wet, hot, cold. Possible roles of leaves: "catch" sunlight, make food for plant.

3. For each root that you looked at, predict where the plant might live and how its root helps the plant survive.

   Possible environments: dry, wet, hot, cold. Possible roles of roots: transport water, give support, anchor plant, store food.

Name ______________________ Date __________

QUICK LAB

FOR SCHOOL OR HOME

Lesson 2

# Leaves

**Hypothesize** In what ways are the leaves that are important to you alike? In what ways are they different? Write a **Hypothesis:**

Possible hypothesis: Edible leaves have the same basic structures such as veins and petioles, but may be different sizes, shapes, textures, and colors.

## Materials

- various plant leaves that you eat
- hand lens

## Procedure

1. Collect a variety of different leaves that you eat as food.
2. **Observe** Examine them with a hand lens. Draw what you see.
   Drawings may show: All of the leaves have veins and petioles. The leaves have different sizes and shapes. Most of the leaves are a shade of green. Some leaves are very smooth and others are rough.

## Drawing Conclusions

3. In what ways are the leaves you observed alike? In what ways are they different?
   Possible answer: All have veins and petioles. The leaves are different in size, shape, texture, and color.
4. Compare the leaves you examined with the leaves your classmates looked at. In what ways are your leaves similar to theirs? In what ways are they different? Record your observations.
   Possible answer: The leaves may differ in size, shape, texture, and color, but all have the same basic parts.

Name ______________________ Date ____________

QUICK LAB

FOR SCHOOL OR HOME

Lesson 2

**5. Going Further** What parts of plants are vegetables? What parts of plants do people eat? Write and conduct an experiment.

My Hypothesis Is:

Possible hypothesis: People eat all parts of a plant.

My Experiment Is:

Bring in vegetables that are not leaves. Note the similarities and differences.

Categorize the vegetables by plant part using a table.

My Results Are:

Students might conclude that we eat all parts of plants. Some vegetables are stems (asparagus, potatoes), some are seeds (peas, corn), some are buds (broccoli, cauliflower), and some are roots (carrots, beets). A vegetable may be more than one plant part. For example broccoli is both a stem and bud. Some of the plant parts we eat might be fruits (tomato, squash).

| Root | Stem | Bud | Fruit | Seed |
|---|---|---|---|---|
| beets | asparagus | broccoli | tomatoes | peas |
| carrots | potatoes | cauliflower | squash | corn |
| radishes | broccoli | | green beans | |
| sweet potatoes | | | eggplant | |
| turnips | | | | |
| | | | | |





Use with textbook page A25

Name ______________________ Date ____________

**Explore Activity**

Lesson 3

# What Does Light Do for a Plant?

**Hypothesize** How will a plant change if it does not get sunlight for several days? Why does it change?

Write a **Hypothesis:**

Possible hypothesis: Leaves will change color and die if they do not get sunlight. Sunlight helps plants make food.

## Materials

- growing plant (window plants from home or plants from an aquarium)
- opaque paper or aluminum foil

## Procedure

1. Cover part of a leaf of a growing plant. Be sure to wash your hands after handling the plants.
2. **Using Variables** Cover a least four different leaves of the plant in the same way.
3. Place the whole plant in a window that gets lots of light.
4. **Experiment** Remove the foil from one leaf after one class period. How is that leaf different from the uncovered leaves? Record your observations. Then cover the leaf again.

   Possible observation: The leaf has not changed noticeably.

5. **Experiment** Continue your observations. Remove the foil from another leaf after one day, another after two days, and another after a week. Record your observations. Replace the foil each time.

   Possible observation: The leaves slowly turn yellow or lose their green color.

## Drawing Conclusions

1. **Observe** After one class period, how was the leaf you had just uncovered different from the uncovered leaves?

   Possible answer: The leaf had not changed noticeably.

**2. Interpret Data** How did the difference you noticed change after a day, two days, and a week?

Possible answer: The leaves lose more of their green color the longer they are covered.

**3. Infer** How do light and darkness affect the growth of leaves?

Possible answer: Leaves in the light stay green and grow. Leaves kept in the dark lose their color and start to die..

**4. Going Further: Use Variables** Remove the coverings from the four leaves and observe them for another week. How do these leaves respond to being uncovered?

Possible answer: The leaves should begin to regain their green color. Eventually, the differences between the leaves will disappear.

**Inquiry**

Think of your own questions that you might test. What are the best levels of light for geraniums and impatiens?

My Question Is:

Possible question: What are the best light conditions for geraniums and impatiens?

How I Can Test It:

Possible test: Obtain 2 each of young, healthy geranium and impatien plants. Place one of each in bright sunlight and one of each in a location with indirect or low light. Observe the plants growth and appearance over several weeks.

My Results Are:

Possible answer: Geraniums grow best in bright sunlight. Impatiens grow best in indirect or low light.

Name ____________________ Date ____________

Alternative Explore

Lesson 3

# In the Dark

## Procedure

1. Obtain two similar plants.
2. Place one plant in a dark area, such as a closet. Place the other plant in a sunny area.
3. Observe the plants each day over the course of two weeks and record your observations. Remember to give both plants the same amount of water.

### Materials

- two similar plants

| Day | Plant in a Sunny Place | Plant in a Dark Place |
|---|---|---|
| | | |
| | | |
| | | |
| | | |
| | | |
| | | |
| | | |
| | | |
| | | |
| | | |

## Drawing Conclusions

1. After two weeks, how did the plants look?

   The plant from the sunny area looked healthy. The plant in the dark was a paler shade of green. Its stem grew long and thin.

2. What do you think will happen to the plant that was in the dark if you put it in the light?

   Answers will vary, but students will likely predict that the plant will become a deeper shade of green.

Name ______________________ Date ______________

**Process Skill Builder**
Lesson 3

# Experiment

## Why Leaves Change Color

To find out why leaves change color in autumn, the first thing you might do is figure out what changes occur in the fall that might cause leaves to change color. Scientists call such changes *variables*. You might identify two of these variables as the amount of daylight and the temperature, both of which go down in the fall.

Next you would make a guess that seems to make sense about which variable causes leaves to change color. This guess is called a *hypothesis*. It is often made in the form of an *if . . . then . . .* statement. For example, "*If* the plant doesn't get water, *then* it won't grow." To see if your hypothesis is a good idea, you would perform an experiment. That experiment has to be set up so that it gives a clear answer.

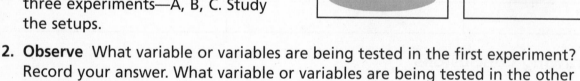

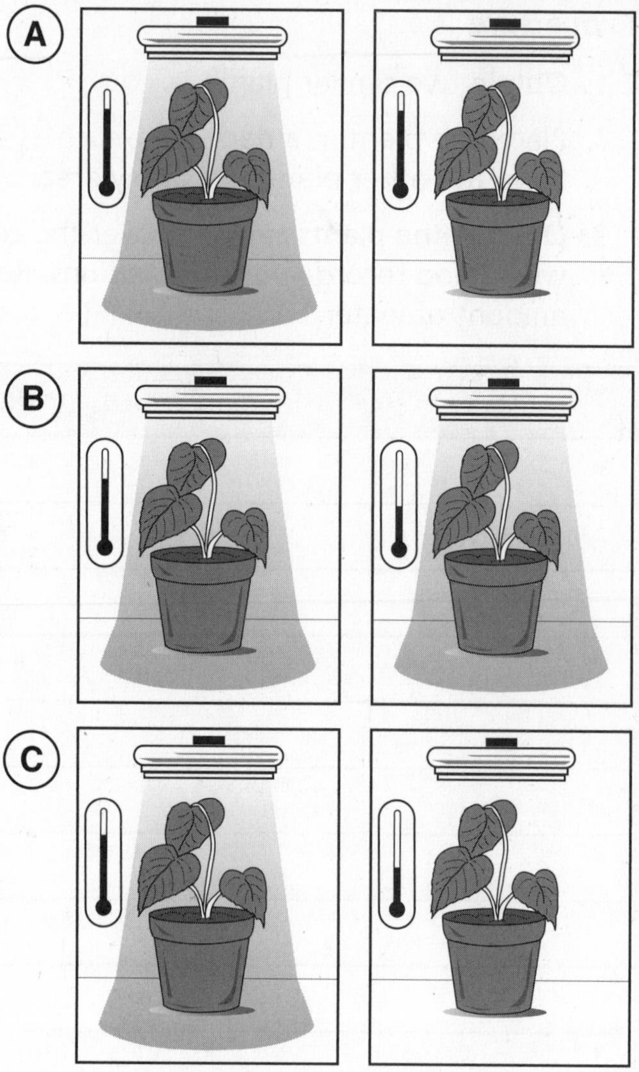


## Procedure

1. Look at the drawings. They show three experiments—A, B, C. Study the setups.
2. **Observe** What variable or variables are being tested in the first experiment? Record your answer. What variable or variables are being tested in the other two experiments?

   Experiment A: light; experiment B: temperature; experiment C: light and temperature.

## Drawing Conclusions

1. **Infer** Which experiment is testing to see whether light causes leaves to change color? Explain.

   Experiment A is using light as a variable because all other variables except light are the same for both plants.

2. **Infer** Which experiment is testing to see whether temperature causes leaves to change color? Explain why.

   Experiment B is using temperature as a variable because all other variables except temperature are the same for both plants.

3. **Infer** Which experiment will not give a clear answer? Explain why not.

   Experiment C will not give a clear answer. Since both light and temperatures are variables here, the color change can be the result of either one of the variables.

Name______________________________ Date______________

Explore Activity
Lesson 4

# How Do Mosses Get Water?

**Hypothesize** Why do ferns grow tall while mosses grow only very close to the ground? How do the parts of mosses help them live where they do?

Write a **Hypothesis:**

Possible hypothesis: Ferns grow tall because they have vascular tissue which can transport water over sizeable distances. Mosses are short because they do not have vascular tissue and cannot transport water over significant distances. Mosses have a very large surface area of cells which absorb water from the environment.

## Materials

- hand lens
- forceps
- dropper
- 3 microscope slides
- coverslip
- microscope
- moss plant

## Procedure

1. **Observe** Place a moss on a paper towel. Use a hand lens to find its rootlike, stemlike, and leaflike parts. Record your observations.

   Possible observation: The stemlike and leaflike parts are green and very small. The rootlike parts look like hairs.

2. **Measure** Use the forceps to remove a leaflike part. Make a wet-mount slide of the part. Observe its cells using the microscope on low power. Determine how thick the leaflike part is by moving the focus up and down. Use the scale in the microscope.

3. **Observe** Find a capsule-shaped object at the end of the brownish stalk. Observe it with the hand lens. Place the capsule on a slide. Add a drop of water. Place a second slide on top of the capsule. Press down on the top slide with your thumb and crush the capsule. Carefully remove the top slide and place a coverslip over the crushed capsule. Examine the released structures under low power. On a separate sheet of paper, draw what you see.

   Possible observation: round structures released from the capsule.

Name ______________________ Date ____________

**Explore Activity**
**Lesson 3**

## Drawing Conclusions

1. **Observe** Which parts of the moss are green? Explain why they are green.

   Possible answer: The leaflike structures of the moss are green because they contain chlorophyll.

2. **Observe** How many cell layers make up the leaflike structure?

   Possible answer: Students should see one or two layers of cells.

3. **Interpret Data** What structures anchor the moss plant? What was the capsule?

   Possible answer: The rootlike structures anchor the plant. Tiny particles are in the capsule.

4. **Going Further: Predict** What do you think the objects inside the capsule do? How would you set up an experiment to test your prediction?

   Possible answer: The particles, make new plants. Students can plant the particles to find out if they grow into plants.

### Inquiry

Think of your own questions that you might like to test. How do cells of mosses compare with other plant cells?

My Question Is:

Possible question: Are the cells of moss plants similar to the cells of other plants?

How I Can Test It:

Possible test: View moss and another plant's cells under a microscope and compare the structures.

My Results Are:

Possible answer: Yes, both are box-like cells containing a nucleus, cytoplasm, and chloroplasts.

Name ______________________ Date __________

Alternative Explore
Lesson 4

# Parts of Mosses

## Procedure

1. Your teacher will give your group some pictures of mosses.
2. In the pictures, find the rootlike hairs, the stemlike part, and the leaflike part. Record your observations.

   Students should make observations about the color, shape, and size of these parts.

3. Look at illustrations of moss cells and the inside of a spore capsule. Draw what you see.

## Materials

- pictures and diagrams of different mosses and parts of mosses

## Drawing Conclusions

1. Is there anything in the pictures of moss plants to tell you how large the plants are? If so, describe their size.

   Mosses are very small, only an inch or two high.

2. Which part of a moss plant looks like it lasts longer: the green part or the spore case? Explain.

   The green part, because it looks sturdy compared to the thin stalk of the spore case.

Name ______________________ Date ____________

QUICK LAB

FOR SCHOOL OR HOME

Lesson 4

# Ferns

**Hypothesize** In what ways are ferns and mosses alike and different? Examine a fern and compare the results to those from the Explore Activity. Write a **Hypothesis:**

Possible hypothesis: Mosses and ferns both produce spores, but only ferns have a vascular system.

## Materials

- fern plant
- fern leaf with spore cases
- microscope
- microscope slide
- toothpick
- water

## Procedure

1. **Observe** Carefully examine the whole fern plant. Look at the stem. Observe how the leaves grow from the stem. Find veins in the leaves. Draw what you see.

   Possible answers: Students should draw leaves growing in pairs along the stem. Student drawings should show veins clearly visible in the leaves.

2. **Observe** Find a leaf whose bottom is covered with brownish spots. These are spore cases.
3. **Experiment** Place a drop of water on a clean slide. Use a toothpick to scrape one of the spore cases into the drop of water.
4. **Observe** Examine the spore case under the low power of a microscope. What does the spore case contain?

   Students will observe spores inside spore cases.

Name ______________________ Date __________

QUICK LAB

FOR SCHOOL OR HOME

Lesson 4

## Drawing Conclusions

5. **Infer** What do fern and mosses have in common?

   Possible answer: Mosses and ferns both have spores.

6. **Going Further** What is the function of fern spores? How can you demonstrate this? Write and conduct an experiment.

   My Hypothesis Is:

   Possible hypothesis: Fern spores produce new plants through asexual reproduction.

   My Experiment Is:

   Possible experiment: Plant some fern spores and observe after some time.

   My Results Are:

   Possible Answer: Fern spores make new plants.

Name ______________________ Date ____________

Explore Activity
Lesson 5

# How Do Seed Plants Differ?

**Hypothesize** Have you ever noticed the differences in plant leaves? Are some leaves larger than others? How do these differences help the plant survive?

Write a **Hypothesis:**

Possible hypothesis: Plants with different leaf sizes, shapes, and textures exhibit different rates of water loss.

## Materials

- small pine seedling or other conifer
- grass plant
- garden plant or house plant, such as geranium
- hand lens
- microscope slide
- coverslip
- microscope

## Procedure

1. **Observe** Examine each plant. Use the hand lens to examine a leaf from each one. On a separate piece of paper, draw each leaf, and label it with the name of the plant it came from.
2. **Observe** Remove a part of the lower epidermis from the grass leaf. Make a wet-mount slide. Examine the slide under low power.
3. **Communicate** On a separate piece of paper, draw what you observe.
Drawings should reflect boxed structures.
4. **Observe** Repeat step 2 with a pine needle and a houseplant leaf (such as a geranium). On a separate piece of paper, draw what you observe. Drawings should be similar to ones in step 2, but patterns should differ.

## Drawing Conclusions

1. **Interpret Data** How are the leaves of the three plants alike? How are the leaves of the three plants different from one another?
Possible answer: All the leaves are green, have stomata, and have a vascular system. The grass blade is thin and the geranium leaf is broad. The pine leaves are like needles and feel waxy. The vascular tissues have different patterns. The grass has parallel veins and the geraniums veins look like a net.

Name ______________________________ Date ____________

Explore Activity
Lesson 5

2. **Infer** Which one of the plants do you think is least like the other two? Explain your reasoning.

Possible answer: The pine, because its leaves are like needles and its veins are not parallel or netted.

3. **Going Further: Experiment** Predict which of the plants you examined could survive best in a dry environment. How do you think the plant's leaves would help it do this? Design an experiment that would test your prediction.

Possible answer: The pine, because the small, wax-coated, needlelike leaves would help conserve water. Possible experiment: Tie plastic bags around part of each plant, water each the same, then compare the amount of water collected inside each bag.

**Inquiry**

Think of your own questions that you might like to test. How are stomata related to water loss in the leaf?

My Question Is:

Possible question: Are differences in water lost by a leaf related to differences in the size and shape of the stomata?

How I Can Test It:

Possible test: Examine the stomata in grass, pine, and geranium leaves. Then experiment to see how much water each kind of plant loses (see #3 above). Compare amount of water loss to size of stomach to see if there is a relationship.

My Results Are:

Possible answer: Yes, differences in water loss may be due to differences in size and shape of the stomata. The stomata in pine needles are sunken.




Use with textbook page A57

Name ______________________ Date ____________

Alternative Explore

Lesson 5

# Compare Leaves of Seed Plants

**Materials**

- leaves from three different kinds of seed plants
- crayons
- paper

## Procedure

1. Obtain three different leaves.
2. Place one of the leaves between two pieces of paper. Rub a crayon over the top sheet of paper above the leaf.
3. Label the rubbing with the name of the plant.
4. Repeat the procedure with the other two leaves.
5. Draw the vein patterns that you can see in the rubbings.

## Drawing Conclusions

1. Which plant has the largest leaf?

   Answers will vary depending on the plants used.

2. Which plant has the thickest leaf?

   Answers will vary depending on the plants used.

3. Are the vein patterns the same in all three leaves? Describe the patterns.

   Answers will vary depending on the plants used. Vein patterns may be branched and netted or in parallel lines.

# Observe

## Flowering Plants

In this activity you will observe flowering plants in order to classify them. That is, you will examine several plants and try to determine whether each is a monocot or a dicot. As you examine each plant sample, refer to the chart below to help you classify the sample.

**Materials**

- sample leaves and flowers from various angiosperms

## Procedure

1. **Observe** Get together with a few of your classmates and go on a leaf-and-flower-collecting field trip. (Make sure to avoid poison ivy, poison oak, and poison sumac leaves. Your teacher can tell you how to spot them.)
2. **Observe** Find a number of different angiosperms. Try to get a sample of a leaf and flower from each plant. If you can't get a flower, a leaf will do.
3. **Interpret Data** Look at the chart of Characteristics of Monocots and Dicots. It will give you clues on how to tell if the sample leaves and flowers you chose are monocots or dicots.

**Characteristics of Monocots and Dicots**

| Characteristics | Monocots | Dicots |
|---|---|---|
| Cotyledons | 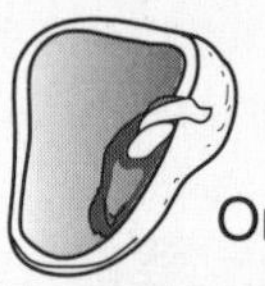 One | 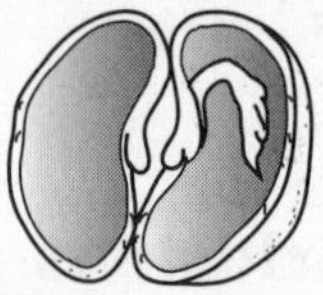 Two |
| Leaf veins | 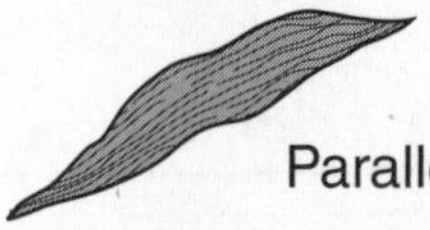 Parallel | 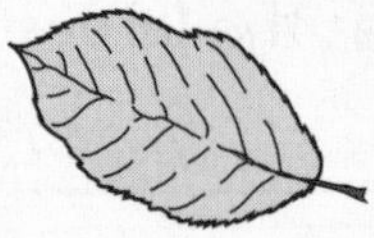 Branched |
| Flower parts |  Multiples of three |  Multiples of four or five |
| Vascular system | Scattered in bundles  |  In rings |

Name ______________________ Date ____________

**Process Skill Builder**

Lesson 5

## Drawing Conclusions

1. **Observe** Examine the plant parts you have chosen. For each sample leaf, describe how the leaf veins look. For each sample flower, tell how many parts each flower has. Record your answers.

   Answer will vary depending on the leaves and flowers collected.

2. **Classify** Mount the leaves and flowers on a heavy sheet of cardboard, and indicate whether each came from a monocot or a dicot.

Name ________________ Date ________

Explore Activity
Lesson 6

# How Do Flowers Differ?

**Hypothesize** Are all flowers alike? If not, how are flowers different? How are they alike? What do you think plants use their flowers for?

Write a **Hypothesis:**

Possible hypothesis: All flowers are not alike.

They differ in size, shape, color, and scent.

## Materials

- several large flowers from different plants
- hand lens
- forceps
- dropper
- toothpick

### Procedure: Design Your Own

1. Decide how you will compare the flowers you look at. You may choose to look for parts that they seem to have in common. Describe what the parts are and how they differ from plant to plant.

   Possible answer: Flowers have a number of different parts. There are leaflike parts at the base of the flower. They are colored structures. There are stalklike structures. There is a tall structure in the center of the flower. The plant parts differ in size, shape, scent, and color.

2. Begin by removing the outer leaflike parts. Examine them. On a separate sheet of paper, draw what they look like.
3. Remove the petals. Examine them. Draw what they look like.
   Colors and shapes will vary.
4. **Observe** Examine the rest of the flowers as you decide.
   Possible observations: The flower may have a powdery substance. Part of the flower may be sticky.
5. **Communicate** Draw the parts you examined. Each structure should be labeled.





Use with textbook page A69

Name ______________________ Date __________

Explore Activity
Lesson 6

## Drawing Conclusions

1. **Communicate** What color is each flower? What do you think the job of the petals is? How would you design an experiment to find out?

   Possible answer: Petals attract insects. Take the petals off a flower and compare the number of insects visiting it to that for the same type of flower with petals.

2. **Infer** What do you think the various parts of each flower are for? Do you think the same parts of different types of flowers do the same kinds of jobs for their plants?

   Possible answer: The outer leaflike parts protect the petals. The inner parts may make reproductive cells. The same flower parts do the same jobs in different plants.

3. **Going Further: Infer** Why do you think a plant has flowers? Make a hypothesis. Design an experiment to test your ideas.

   Possible answer: Flowers attract insects and produce male and female sex cells. Students might monitor several plants in bloom noting if insects land in the flowers and if seeds develop from the flowers.

### Inquiry

Think of your own questions that you might like to test. How do the inner parts of the flower help the plant to reproduce?

My Question Is:

Do the inner parts of flowers produce plant sex cells?

How I Can Test It:

Pollinate flowers using a cotton swab to transfer pollen from one flower's stamen to another's pistil, then watch for seed formation. Compare the pollinated flower to one that insects are not allowed to visit.

My Results Are:

The pollinated flower produced seeds.

Name ______________________ Date ____________

Alternative Explore

Lesson 6

# Design a Flower

## Procedure

**Materials**

- samples and pictures of different flowers

1. With your partner, look at the pictures and samples. Discuss what each flower part might do.
2. Design your own flower. List the ideas you and your partner have.

   Students' designs should have actual plant parts.

3. Draw your design in the space below.
4. Show your design to the class and explain why you designed the flower this way.

## Drawing Conclusions

1. Does you flower have large petals? Explain your decision.

   Answers will vary depending on design.

2. What are the tall, thin structures in the middle of most flowers for? Did you include any in your model?

   These are reproductive structures. While students do not have to include both male and female parts, they should include one or both in their designs.

Name ______________________ Date ____________

QUICK LAB
FOR SCHOOL OR HOME
Lesson 6

# Inside a Seed

**Hypothesize** What does a seed do? Where does it store its food? How do different seeds compare? Write a **Hypothesis:**

Possible hypothesis: Seeds contain a plant embryo and are the beginning of a new plant's life. Food for the plant embryo is stored in the seed's cotyledons. Seeds may house the embryo and food in different ways.

## Materials

- bean seed (such as a lima bean)
- corn seed
- hand lens
- water

## Procedure

1. Soak the bean seed in water overnight.
2. **Observe** Carefully pull apart the two halves of the seed. Examine the halves with a hand lens. Draw what you see. Students will observe different parts of seeds. Drawings should reflect seed half and its parts.

## Drawing Conclusions

3. **Infer** Which part of the seed is the embryo?

Possible answer: The embryo is the small plantlike structure. The embryo's tiny leaf, stem and root are visible.

4. On your drawing label the seed coat and the cotyledon where food is stored.

The seed coat encases the whole seed. Food is stored in the seed coat.

5. **Communicate** Compare a corn kernel with a lima bean. Describe how its parts are similar to or different from the lima bean.

Possible answer: Both have a tiny plant embryo and stored food for the embryo. The corn seed has only one cotyledon while the bean seed has two cotyledons.

6. **Classify** Which seed is a dicot? Which is a monocot? Explain how you know which is which.

The corn is the seed of a monocot because it has one cotyledon. The bean is the seed of a dicot because it has two cotyledons.

7. **Going Further** Think of your own questions you might like to test. What type of vein structure would you expect for corn and bean leaves?

My Question Is:

Possible question: What kind of vein structure do corn and bean leaves have?

How I Can Test It:

Possible test: Gather leaves from corn and bean plants and examine the veins.

My Results Are:

Possible answer: Since corn is a monocot, its leaves should have parallel veins. The veins in the leaves of a bean plant should be branched since it is a dicot.

Name ________________________ Date ____________

Explore Activity
Lesson 7

# How Do Roots Grow?

**Hypothesize** Do roots always grow "down" no matter how you plant a seed?

Write a **Hypothesis:**

Possible hypothesis: Roots always grow downward.

## Materials

- petri dish (plastic)
- 2 paper towels
- marking pen
- tape
- 4 bean seeds that have been soaked in water overnight

## Procedure

1. Soak two paper towels. Wrinkle the paper towels and place them in the bottom half of the petri dish.
2. Place the four seeds on top of the wet paper towels as shown in diagram 1. Place the seeds so the curved part is turned toward the center of the dish.

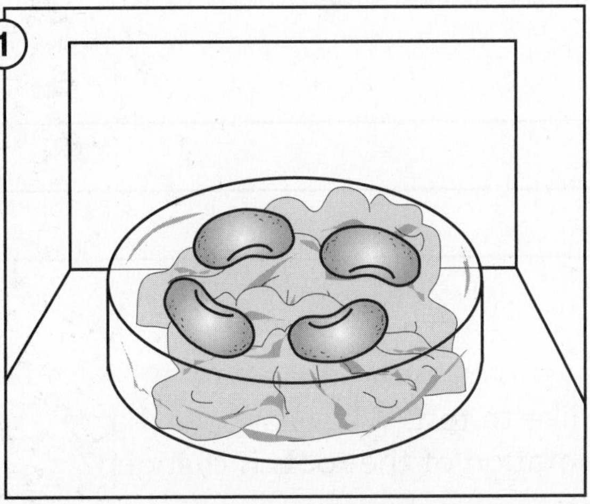


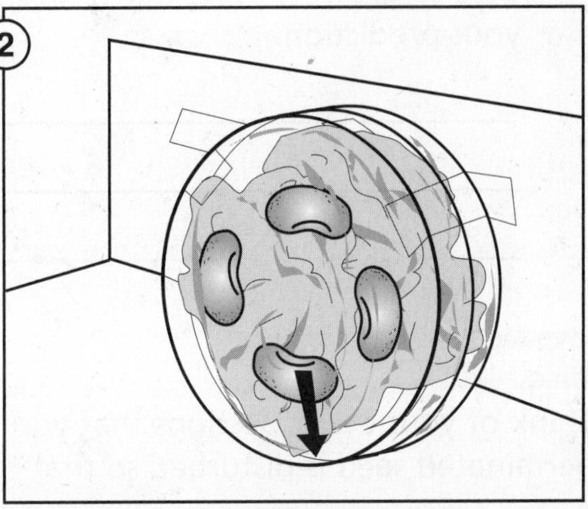


3. Place the top on the petri dish. The top will hold the seeds in the wet paper towels. Seal the top with transparent tape. Draw an arrow on the petri dish with the marking pen as shown in diagram 2. This will show which direction is down. Write the number or name of your group on the petri dish.
4. In a place your teacher provides, stand the petri dish on its edge so the arrow is pointing downward. Tape the petri dish so that it will remain standing. Do not lay the dish down flat.
5. **Predict** Make and record a prediction about the direction you think the roots will grow.

Possible answer: The roots will grow downward.

6. **Communicate** Examine the seeds for the next four days. Record the direction of root growth.

Day 1: The root growth is minimal. Days 2 and 3: The roots may grow in any direction. Day 4: The roots grow downward.

## Drawing Conclusions

1. **Observe** In what direction were the roots growing on day 1? On day 4?

Possible answer: On day 1, the roots were not growing yet or were growing in any direction. By day 4, the roots were growing downward.

2. **Interpret Data** Is your prediction supported by your data?

Possible answer: Yes, the roots of the seeds all grew downward.

3. **Going Further: Predict** What would happen if a seedling were not able to grow its roots down into the soil? Design an experiment to test your prediction.

Possible answer: The seedlings would not get the needed nutrients, water, and stability, and would die. Experiment by growing the seedlings without soil and seeing how long they survive.

## Inquiry

Think of your own questions that you might like to test. What happens if a germinated seed is disturbed so that the orientation of the roots is changed?

My Question Is:

Possible question: If a seedling is rotated so that the roots are no longer pointing down, will the roots change growth direction to head downward again?

How I Can Test It:

After the roots grow down, turn the petri dish upside-down. Observe the direction of the root growth over several days.

My Results Are:

The roots will grow downward.

Name ______________________________ Date ______________

Alternative Explore
Lesson 7

# Which Way Do Corn Plant Roots Grow?

**Materials**

- presoaked corn seeds
- marking pen
- clear, tall plastic cups
- paper towels

## Procedure

1. Line a clear plastic cup with damp paper towels.
2. Place 5 soaked corn seeds between the paper towel and the side of the cup.
3. The seeds should be halfway between the bottom and the rim of the cup. Turn the seeds so that the pointed end of each one points in a different direction.
4. Use the marking pen to number the seeds.
5. Observe the growth of roots over the next few days. In the table, make drawings of each seed each day. Note the direction of the roots.

| Day | Seed 1 | Seed 2 | Seed 3 | Seed 4 | Seed 5 |
|---|---|---|---|---|---|
| | | | | | |
| | | | | | |
| | | | | | |
| | | | | | |

## Drawing Conclusions

1. At the beginning, in what direction did the roots grow?

   Straight out from the top of the seed.

2. After a few days in what direction did the roots grow?

   downward

3. What can you conclude about how roots grow?

   No matter how they start out, the roots grow downward.

Name ______________________ Date ____________

QUICK LAB

FOR SCHOOL OR HOME

Lesson 7

# Plants Compete for Light

**Hypothesize** Do some plants need more light than others? Can some plants survive in shady areas? Write a **Hypothesis:**

Possible hypothesis: Some plants need more light than others do to survive.

## Materials

- grass seed
- ivy plant
- various houseplants
- paper cup
- soil
- camera (optional)

## Procedure

1. Collect samples of various houseplants that grow to different widths and heights.
2. Plant them, with some grass seed, in soil in a paper cup. Record the types of plants you used.

   Answer will vary.

3. **Observe** Examine your plants over the next few days. Draw or photograph their progress. Plants will vary in width and height.

## Drawing Conclusions

4. **Observe** Which plants are being shaded by others? Are the plants in the shade doing as well as the plants that are getting more light?

   Possible answer: Students may observe that the plants shaded by other plants are not growing as well.

5. **Hypothesize** Design an experiment to test which plants need more light to grow. How could you determine if these plants have anything else in common?

   Students might grow duplicates of various types of plants under strong light, medium light, and shade to see which plants thrive in each condition. To find other common traits, students might examine the different parts of plants, possibly using a hand lens and microscope

**6. Going Further** The previous experiment demonstrated that plants require different intensities of light to thrive. Are plants also sensitive to the amount of time they are exposed to light? Write and conduct an experiment.

My Hypothesis Is:

Possible hypothesis: Plants are sensitive to the amount of time that they are exposed to light.

My Experiment Is:

Possible experiment: Set duplicates of various types of plants under the same intensity of light for a different amount of time each day. For example: Select two geraniums and two violets. Leave one of each on a sunny window sill all day for a week or two. During the same time, set the other geranium and violet on the same window sill for only three hours each day, then move these two plants to a shady location. Water the plants equally. Note the condition of the plants over time.

My Results Are:

Possible answer: Given a full day of Sun, the geranium thrived, as did the violet, which was given only a few hours of Sun each day. Both the geranium that received limited Sun and the violet that received a full day of Sun did not look as healthy. In conclusion, plants are sensitive to the amount of time that they are exposed to light.

Name________________________ Date____________

Explore Activity
Lesson 8

# How Are Animals Classified?

**Hypothesize** Are animals grouped by their visual characteristics? Test your ideas.

Write a **Hypothesis:**

Possible hypothesis: animals can be grouped by body parts such as number of legs or horns.

**Materials**

- 25 pictures of animals
- 5 sheets of paper
- tape
- scissors

**Procedure** BE CAREFUL! Be careful using scissors.

1. Cut out 25 animal pictures from old magazines.
2. **Classify** Decide on a trait for grouping the pictures. You may group the pictures into three or more groups.
3. **Communicate** Write your reason for placing the pictures in each group.

   Answers will vary.

4. **Infer** Have your classmates determine the basis you used to group the pictures.

## Drawing Conclusions

1. Which trait was used most often for grouping the pictures?

   Answers will vary.

2. **Infer** What is the best method for grouping the animals?

   Answers will vary.

3. **Going Further: Infer** Why do you think scientists all over the world use a single system for grouping organisms?

Possible answer: It makes classification of newly discovered organisms easier.

## Inquiry

Think of your own question that you might like to test. How else could you classify animals? Might you classify them using their shapes and skin textures?

My Question Is:

Possible question: Can I classify animals by feeling their shapes and textures?

How I Can Test It:

Possible answer: Describe easily identifiable animals such as elephants or lions to a classmate. Ask them to guess the animal based on the description.

My Results Are:

Possible answer: Animals can be identified by their shapes and textures.

Name ______________________________ Date ____________

Alternative Explore

Lesson 8

# Animal Traits

## Procedure

1. Choose two different kinds of animals.
2. Draw a Venn diagram comparing and contrasting the traits of both animals. In each circle, list the traits the two animals do not have in common. Where the circles overlap, list the traits the two animals share.

   Drawings should show two circles with overlapping area. Traits listed will vary but should be correctly placed.

## Drawing Conclusions

3. Compare diagrams with a partner. What traits do all four of your animals share?

   Be sure that students' comparisons accurately list different traits.

Name ______________________________ Date ____________



# Classify

## Using a Key

How should an animal be classified? Into what group of animals should it be placed?

One way to classify organisms is by using a *classification key*. A classification key lists choices describing characteristics of organisms. It is a series of pairs of statements with directions to follow. These directions will eventually lead you to the identity of the organism you have chosen.

## Procedure

1. **Observe** Use the classification key to identify the birds shown on page A100 of your textbook. Starting with the first pair of statements, choose the one that applies to the bird you picked.
2. **Interpret Data** Follow the statement's directions. It will lead you to another pair of statements.
3. Keep following the directions until you come to the identity of the bird you chose.

### Key to Birds

**1.** Webbed feet . . . . . . . . . . . . Go to 3.
No webbed feet . . . . . . . . . Go to 2.

**2.** Hooked bill . . . . . . . . . . . . . Red-tailed Hawk
No hooked bill . . . . . . . . . . Cardinal

**3.** Flat bill . . . . . . . . . . . . . . . . . Mallard Duck
No flat bill . . . . . . . . . . . . . . Go to 4.

**4.** Pouch . . . . . . . . . . . . . . . . . . Brown Pelican
No pouch . . . . . . . . . . . . . . Red-faced Cormorant

Name ____________________ Date __________

**Process Skill Builder**
Lesson 8

## Drawing Conclusions

1. **Interpret Data** What did you notice about each pair of statements?

   Possible Answer: Each statement is an either/or statement.

2. **Classify** What birds did you identify using the key?

   A red-tailed hawk, a cardinal, a brown pelican, a mallard duck, and a red-faced cormorant.

3. Do you think this key would be helpful in identifying birds in your neighborhood? Explain.

   Possible Answer: No, because it only works for 5 specific birds.

Name ______________________ Date ____________

Explore Activity
Lesson 9

# How Do Sow Bugs Adapt to Their Environment?

**Materials**
- 10 sow bugs
- tray
- paper towels
- water

**Hypothesize** Do animals such as sow bugs adapt to their environments? Test your ideas. Write a **Hypothesis:**

Possible hypothesis: sow bugs adapt to environmental changes in temperature, crowding, and food supply.

**Procedure** **BE CAREFUL!** Handle live animals with care. Wash your hands well when you finish this activity.

1. **Observe** Place a sow bug in the center of the tray, and observe it. What traits does it have that enable it to live in the soil and under decaying wood or leaves? Record your observations.

   Traits include hard overlapping plates on their backs, a flattened body, brownish or slate gray color, and seven pairs of legs.

2. **Observe** Touch the sow bug. How does it react?

   Sow bugs do not react to touch. If using pillbugs in their place, the bug will curl into a ball when touched.

3. **Experiment** Place all of the sow bugs in the center of the tray. Do the animals tend to stay together?

   Answers may vary. The sow bugs may scatter in all directions.

4. **Experiment** Move the sow bugs to one end of the tray. Dampen three or four paper towels, and place them in the opposite end of the tray. Observe for several minutes. Record your observations. When the animals move, do they tend to move faster in the dry section or wet section of the box?

   They tend to move toward the wet end and move slower there. NOTE: This change may not occur on very humid days.

Name______________________________ Date____________

Explore Activity
Lesson 9

## Drawing Conclusions

1. **Infer** How do sow bugs protect themselves?

Possible answers: The plates protect their bodies; they huddle to conserve moisture; pillbugs roll into a ball.

2. **Infer** Can the behavior of sow bugs when exposed to moisture be related to their survival? If so, how?

Yes, sow bugs gravitate toward moisture. They must stay moist to survive.

3. **Going Further: Experiment** Design an experiment to test the reactions of sow bugs to light. Record your results.

Possible answer: Place sow bugs in a box that is half in light and half shaded. Then observe.

## Inquiry

Think of your own question that you might to test. How might the sow bugs react to a predator?

My Question Is:

Possible question: How might the sow bugs react to a predator?

How I Can Test It:

Possible test: Place a predator on the tray and observe.

My Results Are:

Possible results: The sow bugs curl into a ball.





Use with textbook page A105

Name ______________________ Date __________

Alternative Explore

Lesson 9

# Earthworms and Light

## Procedure

BE CAREFUL! Be careful handling live animals.

Wash your hands well when you finish this activity.

1. Fill the jar three-quarters full with moist soil. Place a tablespoon of cornmeal on top.
2. Now add the earthworms. Cover the top of the jar with foil.
3. After 24 hours, take off the foil. Write your observations of the earthworms.

   The earthworms have moved to the center of the dirt.
4. Replace the foil. Cover the outside of the jar with the dark paper.
5. Wait another 24 hours. Take off the foil and paper. Where are the earthworms now?

   The earthworms have moved toward the sides of the jar.

### Materials

- 3 earthworms
- moist soil
- plastic jar
- foil
- dark paper
- cornmeal
- tablespoon

## Drawing Conclusions

1. Describe how the earthworms respond to light.

   They avoid the light. When light was coming into the jar, the earthworms moved to the center.
2. Why do the earthworms react this way to light?

   They avoid it to preserve moisture. Earthworms must stay moist to survive.

Name ______________________ Date ____________

QUICK LAB
FOR SCHOOL OR HOME
Lesson 9

# Find the Hybrid Cat

**Hypothesize** Do hybrids exhibit traits of their parents? Test your ideas. Write a **Hypothesis:**

Possible hypothesis: You can see traits of both parents in a hybrid.

**Materials**

- pictures of Persian, Himalayan, and Siamese cats

## Procedure

1. **Observe** Look at the picture of the Siamese cat on page A113 of your textbook. What traits do you think it has been bred for?

   coloring (light body with darker points—face, ears, paws); large ears; slanted eyes; short hair

2. **Observe** Look at the picture of the Persian cat on page A113. What traits do you think it has been bred for?

   long, white fur; short, heavy legs; rounded eyes; small, flattened face

3. **Observe** Look at the picture of the Himalayan cat on page A113. What traits do you think it has been bred for?

   Persian-like body; Siamese coloring (light body with darker points); long hair

## Drawing Conclusions

4. **Infer** Which cat do you think is the hybrid? Explain your answer.

   The Himalayan is the hybrid. It shares some traits with both the Persian and the Siamese.

5. **Going Further: Predict** Choose two different but related animals as possible hybrid parents. What desirable traits might the offspring of these two animals have?

   Answers will vary.

Name ______________________ Date __________

Explore Activity
Lesson 1

# What Do Living Things Need to Survive?

**Materials**

- wide-mouthed, clear container with lid
- washed gravel
- pond water or aged tap water
- water plants
- water snails
- soil
- small rocks
- grass seed and small plants
- earthworms, land snails, sow bugs, or other small land animals that eat plants

**Hypothesize** How do living things interact with each other and their environment? What do living things need in order to survive? How would you design a special environment to test your ideas?

Write a **Hypothesis:**

Possible hypothesis: Living things depend on each other for food. They depend on nonliving things for shelter and for air and water. Possible test: Create a water environment and a land environment and include plants, animals, food, water, and soil.

**BE CAREFUL!** Handle animals and plants gently.

## Procedure: Design Your Own

1. For a water environment, add thoroughly washed sand or gravel to the jar. Fill the jar with water. Add a few floating plants, rooted plants with floating leaves, and submerged plants. Add water snails.
2. For a land environment, place a layer of gravel on the bottom of the jar. Cover the gravel layer with a layer of moistened soil. Add plants, and plant grass seeds. Add earthworms, sow bugs, and snails.
3. Place each jar in a lighted area but not in direct sunlight.
4. Cover each jar with its own lid or with a piece of plastic wrap. Record the number and types of living things you used.

______________________________

______________________________

______________________________

Name ______________________ Date ____________



5. **Observe** Examine your jars every other day. Record your observations on another sheet of paper.
Students should observe the growth and general health of the living things in their environments.

## Drawing Conclusions

1. **Infer** What are the nonliving parts of your system? What are the living parts of your system?
Nonliving: water, sand, soil, gravel, rocks, sunlight, jar; living: plants, snails, earthworms, sow bugs

2. **Infer** What do the living things need to survive? How do you know?
They need air, water, food, light, shelter, and warmth. Both kinds of environments thrive when provided with these things.

3. **Going Further: Experiment** How could you design an environment that contains both land and water areas?
Possible answer: Design a beach or a pond environment.

## Inquiry

Think of your own questions that you might like to test. How do changes in conditions in an environment affect the organisms in the environment?

My Question Is:
Possible answer: What is the effect of raising the temperature of the environment?

How I Can Test It:
Possible answer: Place the jar in a warmer area and observe what happens.

My Results Are:
A slight increase in temperature is likely to increase plant growth, especially in the water environment. A large increase in temperature may kill some of the organisms in the environment.

Name____________________ Date__________

Alternative Explore

Lesson 1

# Plant Needs

In 1699, a scientist named John Woodward did an experiment in plant growth. He weighed four plants and put each in a flask. He added different water samples to each one—rainwater, muddy river water, drain water, and tap water with partly rotted leaves. He weighed the plants to see which had increased its weight the most.

**Materials**

- 4 water mint plants
- 4 flasks
- marking pen
- 4 different water samples
- scale
- ruler

## Procedure

1. With your group, decide on four different water samples you will use to do an experiment like Woodward's.
2. With your group, decide how you will carry out your experiment. Write the steps your group plans for the experiment.

   Place plants in flasks. Weigh the flasks and measure the length of the plants. Water each plant with a different water sample. Use an equal volume of water with each plant. After about two weeks, weigh and measure the plants again.

3. Show the plan to your teacher for approval. Then begin to carry out your plan. Use a separate sheet of paper to record your data and observations.

## Drawing Conclusions

1. What four types of water samples did your group decide to test?

   Answers will vary.

2. How did you decide to measure plant growth?

   Answers will vary.

3. Did any plant grow better than others? If so, which one?

   Answers will vary depending on water samples used. Plants grown with decaying plant matter will grow better than plants grown without it.

Name ______________________________ Date ____________

**Process Skill Builder**

Lesson 1

# Use Variables

**Materials**

- ruler

## Vanishing Bald Eagles

The table below shows the average number of bald eagle eggs that hatched in the wild during a 16-year period. It also shows the level of an insecticide in bald eagle eggs during the same period. What is the relationship between these two variables?

Variables are things that can change. In order to determine what caused the results of an experiment, you need to change one variable at a time. The variable that is changed is called the *independent variable*. A *dependent variable* is one that changes because of the independent variable.

**BALD EAGLE EGG-HATCHING DATA**

| Year | 1966 | 1967 | 1968 | 1969 | 1970 | 1971 | 1972* | 1973 | 1974 | 1975 | 1976 | 1977 | 1978 | 1979 | 1980 | 1981 |
|---|---|---|---|---|---|---|---|---|---|---|---|---|---|---|---|---|
| Average number of young hatched (per nest) | 1.28 | 0.75 | 0.87 | 0.82 | 0.50 | 0.55 | 0.60 | 0.70 | 0.60 | 0.81 | 0.90 | 0.93 | 0.91 | 0.98 | 1.02 | 1.27 |
| Insecticide in eggs (parts per million) | 42 | 68 | 125 | 119 | 122 | 108 | 82 | 74 | 68 | 59 | 32 | 12 | 13 | 14 | 13 | 13 |

*pesticide banned

## Procedure

1. **Infer** What is the independent variable in the study? What is the dependent variable in the study?

   The independent variable is the insecticide in the eggs and the dependent variable is the average number of young hatched.

2. **Communicate** On a separate piece of paper, make a line graph showing the average number of young that hatched. Make another line graph showing the amount of insecticide in eggs.

Name ______________________ Date ____________

Process Skill Builder

Lesson 1

## Drawing Conclusions

1. **Use Variables** Based on the graphs, what appears to be the relationship between the amount of insecticide in eggs and the number of young hatched?

   Possible answer: As the amount of insecticide increases, the number of hatchlings decreases.

2. **Hypothesize** Suggest a reason for the relationship.

   Possible answer: The presence of insecticide in the eggs results in the death of some bald eagle eggs.

Name ______________________ Date __________

Explore Activity
Lesson 2

# How Do Populations Interact?

**Materials**

- tape
- string
- population cards, p.53

**Hypothesize** How can changes in a population lead to changes to the ecosystem in which the population lives? What kinds of changes might these be? How might you test your ideas? Write a **Hypothesis:**

Possible hypothesis: Changes in a population affect the populations that eat it and the populations that it eats.

## Procedure

1. Cut out the cards representing the plants and animals in the ecosystem.
2. Label the top of your paper *Sunlight.*
3. Place the plant cards on the paper, and link each to the sunlight with tape and string.
4. Link each plant-eating animal to a plant card. Link each meat-eating animal to its food source. Only two animals can be attached to a food source. Record the links you have made.

   Possible answers: Prairie plants link to sunlight; grasshopper, squirrel link to prairie plants; meadowlark links to grasshopper; and red-tail hawk, coyote link to squirrel.

5. Fire destroys half the plants. Remove four plant cards. Rearrange the animal cards. Remove animal cards if more than two animals link to any one food source. Record the changes you have made.

## Drawing Conclusions

1. **Observe** What has happened to the plant eaters as a result of the fire? To the animal eaters?

   The number of plant eaters decreased. This led to a decrease in the number of meat eaters.

2. **Infer** Half of the plants that were lost in the fire grow back again. What happens to the animal populations?

Possible answer: As more plants are available, the number of plant-eating animals increases, leading to an increase in the number of meat-eating animals.

3. **Experiment** Try adding or removing plant or animal cards. What happens to the rest of the populations?

Answers will vary. Populations depend on each other for food, and their numbers increase or decrease according to the amount of food available.

4. **Going Further: Predict** If plants or prey become scarce, their predators may move to a new area. What will happen to the ecosystem the predators move into?

Possible answer: The predators will increase the consumption of their food sources in the new ecosystem. Their food sources and the populations dependent on them will decrease.

## Inquiry

Think of your own questions you might like to test. How would an ecosystem change if some meat-eating animals were removed from it?

My Question Is:

Possible question: How would an ecosystem change if half of the meat-eating animals were removed from it?

How I Can Test It:

Possible test: Set up an ecosystem, then remove half of the meat-eating animals and rearrange the cards.

My Results Are:

Possible answer: When meat-eating animals are removed, the populations of prey increase. As the numbers of prey increase, their food sources (animal or plant) decrease and populations dependent on these food sources decrease.

Name ____________________ Date ____________

**Explore Activity**

**Lesson 2**

| | | |
|---|---|---|
| **Bison**<br>Food: prairie plants | **Prairie Plants**<br>Food: made from water, carbon dioxide, and sunlight | |
| **Field Sparrow**<br>Food: prairie plants | **Prairie Plants**<br>Food: made from water, carbon dioxide, and sunlight | **Lizard**<br>Food: insects |
| **Prairie Plants**<br>Food: made from water, carbon dioxide, and sunlight | **Pronghorn Antelope**<br>Food: prairie plants | **Racer (snake)**<br>Food: lizards, mice, insects |
| **Meadowlark**<br>Food: crickets, grasshoppers | **Coyote**<br>Food: rabbits, ground squirrels, meadow mice, other rodents | **Prairie Plants**<br>Food: made from water, carbon dioxide, and sunlight |
| **Prairie Plants**<br>Food: made from water, carbon dioxide, and sunlight | **Bullsnake**<br>Food: mice, rabbits, ground squirrels, birds and eggs | **Field Cricket**<br>Food: prairie plants, other insects |
| **Ground Squirrel**<br>Food: prairie plants | **Red-Tailed Hawk**<br>Food: ground squirrels, mice, rabbits, snakes, lizards, small birds | **Badger**<br>Food: ground squir-rels, rabbits, mice, lizards |
| **Prairie Plants**<br>Food: made from water, carbon dioxide, and sunlight | **Grasshopper**<br>Food: prairie plants | **Prairie Plants**<br>Food: made from water, carbon dioxide, and sunlight |
| **Cottontail Rabbit**<br>Food: prairie plants | **Prairie Plants**<br>Food: made from water, carbon dioxide, and sunlight | **Meadow Mouse**<br>Food: prairie plants |

Name ______________________ Date ____________

Alternative Explore

Lesson 2

# Food Chain Model

**Materials**

- construction paper
- tape
- scissors
- reference materials

## Procedure

1. Cut strips of construction paper. The strips will represent the links in a food chain that includes the Sun, plants, a plant-eater, and a meat-eater. Label the links with these four things.
2. Lay out the strips of paper in the order that they should appear in a food chain. Choose specific organisms for each step in your food chain. Use reference materials to select your organisms. List the organisms you chose.

   Possible answer: Plant: corn; plant-eater: grasshopper; meat-eater: sparrow

3. Write the name of each organism on the correct piece of paper.
4. Use tape to make the paper strips into links that form a chain.
5. Share your chain with other students. Look for ways your chains are similar and ways they are different.

## Drawing Conclusions

1. In what ways were all the food chains similar?

   They start with the Sun.

2. In what ways did the food chains differ from one another? Give an example.

   Each student may have chosen different plants and animals to be the links in the chain.



Use with TE textbook page B17

Name ______________________ Date ____________

QUICK LAB

FOR SCHOOL OR HOME

Lesson 2

# Getting Food

**Hypothesize** What living things are in your community? Which are producers? Which are consumers? Write a

**Hypothesis:**

Hypotheses will vary. Plants are producers. Animals are consumers.

## Materials

- **camera (optional)**
- **collecting net (optional)**

## Procedure

1. Take a walk outdoors around your home or school. Choose a community to study. Make a list of the living things you see. Don't include people or domestic animals like dogs, cats, and farm animals. You may want to take photos to complete your observations. Use illustrations to complete step 2.

   Answers will vary. Answers should include plants and animals.

2. **Classify** Organize the organisms into two groups—those that can make their own food (producers) and those that cannot (consumers).

| Producers | Consumers |
|---|---|
| | |
| | |
| | |
| | |
| | |
| | |
| | |
| | |

Name ______________________ Date ____________

QUICK LAB

FOR SCHOOL OR HOME

Lesson 2

## Drawing Conclusions

3. **Classify** Which organisms did you list as producers?

   Answers will vary. The organisms listed should be plants.

4. **Classify** Which organisms did you list as consumers?

   Answers will vary. The organisms listed should be animals.

5. **Communicate** Draw two or more food chains to show how energy moves through this community. Use an extra sheet of paper if necessary.

   Food chains should indicate that energy moves from producers to consumers.

6. **Going Further** How does the community you studied compare to other communities? Plan and conduct an experiment.

   My Hypothesis Is:

   Possible hypothesis: A different community will have different organisms, but both will have producers and consumers.

   My Experiment Is:

   Possible experiment: Repeat the same experiment, this time observing a different community. Compare the food chains in both communities.

   My Results Are:

   Possible answer: The two communities have different organisms, but all the food chains begin with producers and end with consumers.

Name ______________________ Date __________

**Explore Activity**
Lesson 3

# What Happens to Water?

**Materials**

- plastic food container with clear cover
- small bowl or cup filled with water
- small tray filled with dry soil
- paper towel
- 100-W lamp (if available)

**Hypothesize** How can we, and all living things, keep using water every day and not use it all up? How would you experiment to test your ideas?

Write a **Hypothesis:**

Possible hypothesis: Water in the environment is recycled. Water evaporates from oceans, lakes, and so on, eventually returning as rain and snow.

## Procedure

1. Place the dry paper towel, the dry soil, and the bowl of water in the plastic container. Close the container with the lid.
2. **Observe** Place the container under a lamp or in direct sunlight. Observe every ten minutes for a class period. Record your observations.

   Water drops condensed on the inside of the container.

3. Observe the container on the second day. Record your observations.

   Possible answer: Water drops condensed on the inside of the container and dropped onto the soil and paper towel.

## Drawing Conclusions

1. What did you observe the first day? What did you observe the second day?

   Possible answer: On the first day water drops condensed on the inside of the container. On the second day, more water condensed and dropped, wetting the soil and paper towel.

**2. Infer** What was the source of the water? What was the source of the energy that caused changes in the container?

Possible answer: The water on the sides of the container is the same water that was put in the container. Energy from the Sun or lamp heated the water in the bowl, causing it to evaporate.

**3.** What happened to the water?

Possible answer: The water evaporated from the bowl, condensed when it came in contact with the cool container, and fell to the bottom of the container.

**4. Going Further: Infer** How did the water move?

Possible answer: The model demonstrated evaporation from a body of water, condensation in a cool environment, and water drops falling and wetting surfaces.

## Inquiry

Think of your own questions you might like to test. What happens to the salt in ocean water when the water evaporates?

My Question Is:

Possible question: Does salt evaporate with ocean water?

How I Can Test It:

Possible test: Remove the soil and towel from the model. Wash the container, cover, and bowl. Dissolve some salt in warm water and pour it in the bowl. Place another clean bowl in the container. Cover the container and place it in sunlight or under a lamp. Test the water that collects to see if it contains salt.

My Results Are:

The collected water does not contain salt, so salt does not evaporate with ocean water.

Name ______________________ Date __________

Alternative Explore
Lesson 3

# Recycling Water

**BE CAREFUL!** Be careful handling the hot plate and teakettle.

**Materials**

- hot plate
- cookie sheet
- water
- teakettle
- ice cubes
- oven mitts

## Procedure

1. Put water in the teakettle and place the teakettle on the hot plate.
2. Heat the water until you see steam coming out of the teakettle.
3. Place several ice cubes on the cookie sheet.
4. Use the oven mitts to pick up the cookie sheet and hold it over the steam coming from the kettle.
5. Look at the underside of the cookie sheet. Record your observations.

   Water droplets form on the underside of the cookie sheet.

## Drawing Conclusions

1. What happened to the water in the teakettle?

   It changed from a liquid water to steam.

2. What happened to the steam when it hit the cold cookie sheet?

   It changed back into liquid water.

3. What would happen if you shook the cookie sheet?

   Droplets of water would fall from the cookie sheet.

Name ______________________ Date ____________

QUICK LAB

FOR SCHOOL OR HOME

Lesson 3

# Soil Sample

**Hypothesize** How do nutrients get recycled in nature?

Write a **Hypothesis:**

Possible hypothesis: Plants and animals decay, returning nutrients to the soil.

**Materials**

- empty can

## Procedure

**BE CAREFUL!** Do not touch the sharp edges of the can.

1. Go to a wooded area in a park or other location near your school. Find a patch of soft, moist soil.
2. Press a can, open side down, into the soil to get a core sample. You might have to gently rotate the can so it cuts into the soil.
3. **Observe** Carefully remove the core so it stays in one piece. Describe and draw the core.

   Students should describe the composition of soil layers in the core, identifying bits of rock, decaying plant and animal matter, and animals such as worms.

Name ______________________________ Date ____________



## Drawing Conclusions

**4. Infer** From top to bottom, what kind of matter does the core hold? In what order did the layers form?

Possible answer: The top layer has larger pieces of plant and animal material. The decaying bits of plant and animal matter become smaller as you move down into the core. The top layer formed last and the bottom layer formed first.

**5. Infer** Which layer holds the most available nutrients? Explain.

Possible answer: The layer with the smallest pieces of plant and animal material has the most available nutrients. The decayed matter added nutrients to the soil.

**6. Going Further** How do worms help return nutrients to the soil? Write and conduct an experiment.

My Hypothesis Is:

Possible hypothesis: Worms help decompose dead plant material in soil.

My Experiment Is:

Possible experiment: Observe worms in a container of soil with dead plant material for one week.

My Results Are:

The dead plant material disappeared. Worm castings (undigested soil) appeared on the soil. Worms help decompose dead plant matter in soil.

Students will need assistance in setting up an environment for the worms. Give them the following instructions: Place the soil in a jar or clear container. Moisten the soil with a small amount of water. Carefully place the worms on the soil. Gently add thin fruit or vegetable pieces such as apple and carrot peelings. Keep the soil moist during the entire observation period. To reduce water loss, provide an aerated cover for the container. Wrap dark colored paper around the container and secure it with rubber bands. Store the container in a cool place. Remove the paper to observe the worms daily for a week. Add small amounts of water and peelings as needed. Replace the paper and return the container to a cool place.

Name ______________________________ Date ____________

Explore Activity

Lesson 4

# What Controls the Growth of Populations?

## Materials

- 4 small, clean milk cartons with the tops removed
- 40 pinto bean seeds that have been soaked overnight
- soil
- water

**Hypothesize** What kinds of things do organisms need in their environment in order to survive? What happens when these things are limited or unavailable? Test your ideas. Write a **Hypothesis:**

Possible hypothesis: Organisms need food, sunlight, water, and air to survive. Without them organisms become weak and die.

### Procedure

1. Label the cartons 1 to 4. Fill cartons 1 and 2 with dry potting soil. Fill cartons 3 and 4 with moistened potting soil. Fill the cartons to within 2 cm of the top.
2. Plant ten seeds in each carton, and cover the seeds with 0.5 cm of soil.
3. **Use Variables** Place cartons 1 and 3 in a well-lighted area. Place cartons 2 and 4 in a dark place. Label the cartons to show if they are wet or dry and in the light or in the dark.
4. **Observe** Examine the cartons each day for four days. Keep the soil moist in cartons 3 and 4. Record your observations.

   Possible answer: The seeds in moist soil, cartons 3 and 4, sprouted.

5. Observe the plants for two weeks after they sprout. Continue to keep the soil moist in cartons 3 and 4, and record your observations.

   Possible answer: Only the seedlings given water and sunlight, carton 3, thrived. The seedlings given water but no light, carton 4, either grew very little or died.

Name ______________________________ Date ______________

Explore Activity
Lesson 4

## Drawing Conclusions

1. **Communicate** How many seeds sprouted in each carton?

   Answers will vary. Seeds should sprout only in the cartons that were watered, 3 and 4.

2. **Observe** After two weeks how many plants in each carton were still living?

   Answers will vary. The seedlings with sunlight and water, carton 3, should thrive. The seedlings without light, carton 4, will grow very little or die.

3. What factor is needed for seeds to sprout? What is needed for bean plants to grow? What evidence do you have to support your answers?

   Possible answer: Seeds need water to sprout. Bean plants need water and sunlight to grow. Only the seeds given water sprouted. Only the seedlings given water and sunlight continued to grow.

4. **Going Further: Infer** Why did some seeds sprout and then die?

   Possible answer: Seeds contain food for the new seedlings. Once the stored food is depleted, the plants must have light to make their own food.

**Inquiry**

Think of your own questions you might like to test. Do plants need anything other than water and sunlight to thrive?

My Question Is:

Possible question: Do plants need air to survive?

How I Can Test It:

Possible test: Coat the leaves on a plant with petroleum jelly. This prevents air from contacting the leaf. Compare growth with that of a plant whose leaves are not covered.

My Results Are:

The leaves coated with petroleum jelly turned yellow and may have died.

Name ______________________________ Date ______________

Alternative Explore

Lesson 4

# Effect of Water and Light on Plants

**Materials**

- 4 similar plants
- labels
- water

## Procedures

1. Label the plants 1, 2, 3, and 4.
2. Put plants 1 and 2 in a sunny location. Water plant 1 each day. Do not water plant 2.
3. Put plant 3 in a sunny location. Put plant 4 in a dark location. Give both plants the same amount of water.
4. Continue the experiment for two weeks. Make a table to record each day's observations on a separate sheet of paper.

## Drawing Conclusions

1. How did the growth of plants 1 and 2 compare? Explain any differences you saw.

   Plant 1 grew better than plant 2. After two weeks, plant 2 may die. The difference is due to a lack of water for plant 2.

2. How did the growth of plants 3 and 4 compare? Explain any differences you saw.

   Plant 3 grew better than plant 4. The difference is due to the amount of light the plants received. Plant 4 received no light.

3. What can you conclude about the kinds of conditions that plants need to grow?

   Plants need water and light to grow.

Name ______________________ Date ____________

QUICK LAB

FOR SCHOOL OR HOME

Lesson 4

# Playground Space

**Hypothesize** How much playground space does each student in your classroom have? Write a Hypothesis:

Possible hypothesis: Each student has three square meters of playground space.

## Materials

- meterstick
- calculator

### Procedure

1. **Measure** Working in groups, use a meterstick to measure the length and width of your playground.
2. **Use Numbers** Multiply the length by the width to find the area in square meters.

   ______________________________________________

3. Count the number of students in your class.
4. **Use Numbers** To find out how much space each student has, divide the area of the playground by the number of students.

   ______________________________________________

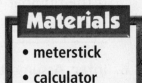

QUICK LAB
FOR SCHOOL OR HOME
Lesson 4

## Drawing Conclusions

5. **Infer** What would happen to the space each student had if the number of students doubled?

   Students would have half the original space.

6. **Infer** Assume two other classes with the same number of students as yours used the playground at the same time as your class. What effect might this have on your class?

   Students would have one third the original space and may not be able to play games that require a lot of space such as jump rope and ball games.

7. **Going Further** How many students can fit in your school? Write and conduct an experiment.

   My Hypothesis Is:

   Possible hypothesis: Three hundred students can fit in my school.

   My Experiment Is:

   Determine the number of classrooms and the average number of desks that fit in a classroom. Multiply the two numbers.

   My Results Are:

   Answers will vary.

# Why Is Soil Important?

**Hypothesize** Why is the soil in one kind of ecosystem different from the soil in another kind of ecosystem? What determines what the soil is like? Write a **Hypothesis:**

Possible hypothesis: The type of soil in an area depends on the type of rock in an area and the climate.

## Materials

- washed sand
- soil
- hydrogen peroxide
- 2 plastic cups
- 2 plastic spoons
- dropper
- goggles
- apron

## Procedure

**BE CAREFUL!** Wear goggles and an apron.

1. Place 1 tsp. of washed sand in a plastic cup.
2. **Observe** Using the dropper, add hydrogen peroxide to the sand, drop by drop. Count each drop. Bubbles will form as the hydrogen peroxide breaks down any decayed matter.
3. **Communicate** Record the number of drops you add until the bubbles stop forming.

   Answers will vary. However, the sand should react with relatively few drops of hydrogen peroxide (compared to the soil or compost).
4. **Experiment** Repeat steps 1–3 using the soil.

## Drawing Conclusions

1. Which sample—soil or sand—gave off more bubbles?

   Possible answer: The soil or compost reacted with more drops of hydrogen peroxide and gave off more bubbles.

**2. Infer** Why was the sand used?

Possible answer: Sand was used for comparison because it contains mostly rock with very little decayed matter.

**3. Infer** Decayed materials in soil release their nutrients to form humus. The amount of humus in soil depends on the rate of decay and the rate at which plants absorb the nutrients. Which sample had more humus?

Possible answer: The soil or compost reacted with more hydrogen peroxide so it had more humus in it.

**4. Going Further: Infer** In which sample could you grow larger, healthier plants? Why?

Possible answer: Plants grown in soil or compost would be healthier than plants grown in sand because soil and compost contain more nutrient-releasing decayed material.

## Inquiry

Think of your own questions you might like to test. How much humus do other soil samples have?

My Question Is:

Possible question: How much decayed material does local soil contain?

How I Can Test It:

Possible test: Take samples from local areas. Repeat the hydrogen peroxide test.

My Results Are:

Answers will vary.

Name ______________________ Date __________

Alternative Explore

Lesson 5

# Testing Soil pH

## Procedure

1. Mix a spoonful of washed sand and a little distilled water in a petri dish.
2. Test the mixture with pH paper. What was the pH of the sand mixture?

   Answers will vary. Students may need assistance in using the pH paper and interpreting the results.

3. Test the other soil sample(s) in the same way. Record your results in the table.

## Materials

- washed sand
- distilled water
- pH test paper
- compost, potting soil, or garden soil
- petri dishes
- spoons

| Sample | pH |
|---|---|
| | |
| | |
| | |
| | |

## Drawing Conclusions

1. Which sample had the highest pH?

   Answers will vary.

2. Which sample had the lowest pH?

   Answers will vary.

3. A low pH means the sample is acidic and not as nutrient rich as soils with a higher pH. Which sample is the most nutrient-rich? Explain your answer.

   Answers will vary depending on the source of the soil. The most nutrient-rich sample is the one with the highest pH.

Name ______________________ Date ____________

QUICK LAB
FOR SCHOOL OR HOME
Lesson 5

# Freshwater Communities

**Hypothesize** Do different organisms live in different locations in aquatic ecosystems? Write a **Hypothesis:**

Possible hypothesis: Different aquatic organisms live in different aquatic environments.

## Materials

- dropper
- microscope slide
- coverslip
- microscope
- at least 3 samples of pond, lake, or stream water
- 3 or more plastic containers with lids

## Procedure

1. Obtain from your teacher samples of pond, lake, or stream water taken at different locations. Use a different container for each sample. Record on the container the location each sample came from.
2. **Observe** Place a drop of water on a slide, and carefully place a coverslip over it. Examine the slide under a microscope.
3. **Communicate** Record the location of each sample and what you see. Use low and high power.

   Organisms will vary. Students should describe the shape, features, and relative size of the organisms. Students should observe different organisms in each sample.

## Drawing Conclusions

4. **Interpret Data** What does this tell you about aquatic ecosystems?

   Different organisms live in different locations in aquatic ecosystems.

Name________________________________ Date____________

QUICK LAB

FOR SCHOOL OR HOME

Lesson 5

5. **Going Further** How do organisms in a different aquatic environment compare to those you examined in the activity? Design and conduct an experiment.

My Hypothesis Is:

Possible hypothesis: Organisms in a different aquatic environment will also be different at different locations, but will be similar to those in the first environment.

My Experiment Is:

Possible experiment: Repeat the procedure in the activity, this time testing a different aquatic ecosystem. Compare the organisms found in both ecosystems.

My Results Are:

Possible answer: The organisms are different at different locations, but are similar to those in the first environment.

Name ______________________ Date __________

**Explore Activity**
**Lesson 6**

# How Do Ecosystems Change?

**Hypothesize** How can ecosystems change? How might an abandoned farm change? Test your ideas. Write a **Hypothesis:**

Possible hypothesis: An abandonded farm may change into a new ecosystem. Plants and animals that lived there may die or leave, and seeds and animals from a nearby ecosystem may inhabit the land.

## Procedure

1. **Observe** Examine the drawing.
2. **Communicate** Describe what you see.

The abandoned farm has tall grasses, and trees are starting to grow there.

## Drawing Conclusions

1. **Infer** What happened to this farm after the owner left and moved to the city?

After the owner left, no one was around to maintain the farm and care for the crops. The building became run-down and the wild grasses and weeds became overgrown.

2. **Infer** Think about how this farm might have looked ten years ago. What kind of plants lived there then?

The farm probably had neatly kept fields of crops such as corn, vegetables, or soybeans.

Name ____________________ Date __________

**Explore Activity**
**Lesson 6**

3. **Interpret Data** How can one ecosystem be changed into another?

   Animals and wind move seeds. Animals move to the new ecosystem.

4. Compare what you think will happen to the abandoned farm with what happened at Mount Saint Helens. In what ways would the changes in the ecosystems be similar? In what ways would they be different?

   New plant and animal life would come from the forest to the abandoned farm as it did at Mount Saint Helens. Some plants and animals from the old farm ecosystem may exist in the new ecosystem, while nearly all plants and animals were destroyed by the eruption of Mount Saint Helens.

5. **Going Further: Predict** Think of another ecosystem that might be changed by nature. Think of an ecosystem that might be changed by humans. Describe how such ecosystems might continue to change over time.

   Natural disasters (fire, floods, volcanic eruptions) destroy ecosystems. Recovery depends on the remaining ecosystem and proximity to a fertile ecosystem. Humans cut forests, mine, plow fields, and pollute. Ecosystem recovery depends on the extent of continued human involvement.

## Inquiry

Think of your own questions you might like to test. How has another ecosystem been changed by nature?

My Question Is:

How has an ecosystem been changed by fire?

How I Can Test It:

Research a major fire and find out how it changed the ecosystem.

My Results Are:

Possible answer: Trees growing in areas surrounding the fire started moving into the ecosystem. The trees have enabled small animals to return.

Name ______________________ Date ____________

Alternative Explore
Lesson 6

# From Pond to Forest

**Materials**

- reference materials

## Procedure

1. Draw a side view of a pond showing plants growing at the edges in the space below. Use extra paper if necessary.

2. Do research to find out what happens to a pond over time as the plants grow.
3. Draw three more pictures of your pond, showing how it could change into a new ecosystem.

Students should draw the pond becoming a marsh with plants at the edge growing in toward the center. The marsh then becomes a field with shrubs and small trees. Lastly, the same area becomes a mature woodland with tall trees.

## Drawing Conclusions

1. What plants grow into the pond at the beginning of this process?

Tall grasses

2. Where do the nutrients for more plants in the pond come from?

The early plants die, and when they rot they add nutrients to the soil.

3. What do you think would be the stage after the woodlands? Explain.

Answers will vary, but students will likely say that the woodlands will remain there unless there is a fire or someone cuts down the trees.

Name ______________________ Date ____________

QUICK LAB

FOR SCHOOL OR HOME

Lesson 6

# Predicting Succession

**Hypothesize** In what areas where you live do you think ecological succession may be taking place? Write a **Hypothesis:**

*Possible hypothesis: Students might suggest a vacant lot, a burnt field or forest, abandoned farmland, or a destroyed shoreline.*

## Procedure

1. **Observe** Identify an area near you where you think ecological succession is taking place.

   *Possible answer: Abandoned property, a burnt field or forest, or a destroyed shoreline*

2. **Communicate** Describe the area. List the evidence you have that indicates ecological succession is taking place.

   *Students should identify the event or environmental change that altered the ecosystem. If possible, students should describe the previous ecosystem. Students should describe all plants and animals in the present ecosystem and how they may indicate the current stage of ecological succession.*

## Drawing Conclusions

3. **Infer** Do you think the succession will be primary or secondary? Explain.

   *Primary succession should be supported by a catastrophic event, such as a fire, that killed nearly all organisms in the original ecosystem. Secondary succession should be supported by describing the previous ecosystem and the major environmental change that has occurred.*

Name ______________________________ Date ____________

QUICK LAB

FOR SCHOOL OR HOME

Lesson 6

4. **Predict** In what order do you think new species will colonize the area? Explain the reasons for your predictions.

Possible answer: Students might suggest grasses and insects; followed by weeds, wildflowers, birds, and small animals; and then trees and more birds and larger animals. Students should explain that each stage can take place only after preceding stages are completed.

5. **Communicate** Describe the climax community that you think will eventually live in the area. Give reasons for your conclusion.

Students should describe the plants and animals that will ultimately inhabit the area until a major environmental disruption occurs. Students might suggest plants that live in nearby climax communities or discuss why the plants and animals would be different from those in nearby climax communities.

6. **Going Further** Is ecological succession taking place in other areas near you? Write and conduct an experiment.

My Hypothesis Is:

Possible hypothesis: Ecological succession is taking place outside my house.

My Experiment Is:

Possible experiment: Observe the area for signs of ecological succession, such as the growth of weeds and grasses.

My Results Are:

Possible answer: There are signs of ecological succession outside my house, but human activities, such as mowing, prevent succession from continuing.

Name ______________________ Date __________

**Process Skill Builder**

Lesson 6

# Infer

## Comparing Ecosystems in Volcanic Areas

In this activity you will collect data and infer about the ecosystems of two volcanic areas.

Data are different kinds of facts. They might include observations, measurements, calculations, and other kinds of information. Scientists collect data about an event to better understand what caused it, what it will cause, and how it will affect other events.

**Materials**

- research books
- Internet

What do these data tell the scientist? The scientist first organizes the data in some way—perhaps a table, chart, or graph. The scientist then studies the organized data and makes inferences. To infer means to form an idea from facts or observations. In this case you will infer about which plants will return to a volcanic area.

## Procedure

1. Collect data on two volcanic areas, such as Mount Saint Helens and the Soufriere Hills volcano on the island of Montserrat or the active volcanoes of Hawaii. Organize the data on a separate sheet of paper.
2. **Communicate** Describe the sequence of events that has taken place.

   Students should describe the ecosystem before the eruption, type of eruption, damage to the surrounding area, ecosystem immediately after the eruption, and ecological succession. The pioneer community should be discussed as well as subsequent communities, if applicable.

3. **Interpret Data** Draw a conclusion about why certain plants return when they do.

   Students should discuss which plants survived the eruption and why, and how new plants/seeds arrived in the desolated area. They should describe the environmental conditions and relate them to the needs of different plants, and discuss how the environmental conditions, such as soil and available sunlight, change over time, and the resulting changes in plant life.

Name ______________________ Date ____________

Process Skill Builder

Lesson 6

## Drawing Conclusions

1. In what ways is succession in the two areas alike? In what ways is it different?

Possible answer: Students should compare pioneer species and communities, and the stage of succession of the areas.

2. **Infer** Why is the succession in these two areas similar or different?

Possible answer: Students should consider the ecosystems before the eruptions, the type of eruptions and resulting desolation, the ecosystems immediately after the eruptions, the proximity of the areas to other fertile ecosystems, and the climates.

3. **Infer** What abiotic factors must you consider when drawing conclusions? What biotic factors must you consider?

Students should consider abiotic factors such as the type of eruption and resulting ground condition (lava flow versus ash layer), and climate. Students should consider biotic factors such as the ecological community that existed before the eruptions, any plant or animal life that may have survived the eruptions, and the desolated area's proximity to other fertile ecosystems.

Name ______________________ Date ____________

**Explore Activity**
Lesson 1

# How Are Earth and the Sun Held Together?

**Materials**

- clay
- string
- scissors
- meterstick
- goggles

**Hypothesize** How does a force hold Earth around the Sun? What would happen if the force let go? Write a **Hypothesis:**

Possible hypothesis: Gravity holds Earth in place. If this force let go, Earth would fly off its orbit in a straight line.

## Procedure

**BE CAREFUL!** Wear goggles. Twirl the model close to the ground.

1. **Make a Model** Cut a 40-cm length of string. Wrap it around a small, round lump of clay in several directions. Tie the ends to make a tight knot. Measure 60 cm of string, and tie it to the string around the ball.
2. **Observe** Spin the ball of clay slowly—just fast enough to keep the string tight and keep the ball off the ground. Keep the ball close to the ground. Describe the path of the ball

   The ball moves in a circular path.

3. **Experiment** At one point while spinning, let the string go. What happens? Describe the path of the ball of clay. Repeat until you get a clear picture of what happens.

   The ball moves in a straight line.

## Drawing Conclusions

1. How did your model represent Earth and the Sun? What represented Earth? Where was the Sun located? How did you represent the force between them?

   Earth was represented by the clay. The Sun was located at the center of the circle, where the person's hand or body was located. The force was represented by the pull of the string.

Name ____________________ Date __________

Explore Activity
Lesson 1

2. **Infer** Explain what happened when you let the string go. Why do you think this happened?

The clay flew off in a straight line because the string no longer connected the spinner and the clay. The force between the Sun and Earth was removed.

3. **Going Further: Use Variables** How would your results change if the mass of the clay was doubled? Tripled? How does the mass affect the pull on the string? Make a prediction. Try it.

Students may predict that if the clay's mass were doubled or tripled, the clay would fly off with double or triple the force but in the same direction. The greater the mass, the stronger the pull on the string.

**Inquiry**

Think of your own questions that you might like to test. What other conditions affect the pull on the string or the path of the released ball of clay?

My Question Is:

Possible answer: How does changing the length of the string affect the path the ball takes?

How I Can Test It:

Possible answer: Repeat the experiment using a longer piece of string to twirl the clay ball.

My Results Are:

Lengthening the string makes the circular path larger. When the ball is released, it still travels on a straight line.





Use with textbook page C5

Name ______________________ Date __________

Alternative Explore
Lesson 1

# Motion of a Planet

**Materials**
- paper plate
- scissors
- marble

## Procedure

1. Place a paper plate on a table. Place a marble in the rut near the rim of the plate.
2. Lift one edge of the plate slightly. Observe what happens. Record your observations.

   The marble rolls in a circle within the plate.

3. Cut the paper plate in half. Place one half of the plate on the table.
4. Place a marble in the rut near the rim of the plate. Lift the edge of the plate slightly. Observe what happens. Record your observations. Draw the path of the marble in the space below. Show the paper plate in your drawing.

   The marble follows the curved edge of the plate until it reaches the cut edge, and then it rolls away in a straight line.

## Drawing Conclusions

1. How is the motion of the marble in the whole paper plate similar to Earth's motion around the Sun?

   The marble travels in a circle, held in place by the rim of the plate.

2. How does cutting the plate in half change the forces on the marble?

   When the plate is cut in half, the rim, which holds the marble in its path, has an opening, and it lets the marble "escape."

3. What would have to happen for Earth's orbit to be like the path of the marble in step 4?

   The Sun's gravity would have to stop working.

Name________________________________ Date______________

QUICK LAB

FOR SCHOOL OR HOME

Lesson 1

# Orbit Times

**Hypothesize** What does the length of time for an orbit depend on? Test your ideas. Write a **Hypothesis:**

Possible hypothesis: A planet's orbit time depends on its distance from the Sun.

**Materials**

- several sheets of graph paper

## Procedure

1. **Communicate** Use graph paper. Draw a bar graph to compare the revolution times for the planets. The vertical axis of the graph represents time. Decide how much time each square on the paper represents. The horizontal axis represents the planets. How many pieces of graph paper will you need? Write your description.

   Answers depend on the graph paper used.

## Drawing Conclusions

2. **Interpret Data** Based on your graph and the data table, what relationship can you find between the length of the year (time) and the planet's location in the solar system?

   The further the planet is from the sun, the longer its year.

3. How could you change your graph to show the relationship even better? What might your new graph reveal?

   Make a line graph of the average distance to the sun versus time for complete orbit around the sun. The graph would show that the length of year increases with increasing distance from the sun.

4. **Use Variables** Draw a line graph on a separate sheet of paper. Let the vertical axis represent time for a complete orbit. Let the horizontal axis represent distance to the Sun. Label each point with the name of its planet.

Name ______________________________ Date ____________

QUICK LAB

FOR SCHOOL OR HOME

Lesson 1

5. **Going Further** Do all the planets travel at the same speed? Calculate each planet's speed. First calculate the distance traveled by treating the orbits as circular and calculating the circumference of the circle ($2\pi r$ where $r$ is the distance to the Sun). Convert the orbit time from days to hours by multiplying the number of days by 24 hours. Calculate the speed by dividing the distance traveled by the hours it takes for a complete orbit around the Sun. Multiply the speed in million km/hour by 1000 to report it in thousand km/hour.

| PLANET | Distance Traveled (million km) | Orbit Time (hours) | Speed (thousand km/hour) |
|---|---|---|---|
| Mercury | 363.8 | 2,112 | 172.3 |
| Venus | 679.8 | 5,376 | 126.5 |
| Earth | 940.0 | 8,760 | 107.3 |
| Mars | 1,431.9 | 16,488 | 86.8 |
| Jupiter | 4,890.2 | 103,992 | 47.0 |
| Saturn | 8,966.1 | 258,216 | 34.7 |
| Uranus | 18,032.7 | 736,440 | 24.5 |
| Neptune | 28,255.5 | 1,444,512 | 19.6 |

Student answers will depend on the value of $\pi$ used.

On a piece of graph paper, plot the average distance to the Sun versus the planet's orbital speed. What is the relationship between a planet's orbital speed and its distance to the Sun? Explain this relationship.

The farther from the Sun a planet is, the slower its orbital speed.

Name______________________________ Date____________

Explore Activity

Lesson 2

# What Makes the Crust Move?

## Materials

- 4–6 matching books (optional)
- layers of clay or modeling compound (optional)
- plastic knife (for use with clay)
- cubes
- wax paper

**Hypothesize** What kind of motion causes an earthquake? Does it always cause destruction? Can it result in anything else? Test your ideas. Write a **Hypothesis:**

Possible hypothesis: Movement below the surface of Earth causes earthquakes. Earthquakes do not always cause destruction. Earthquakes can make new land formations such as mountains.

### Procedure: Design Your Own

1. **Make a Model** Work with a partner to model layers of rock. You may use books, clay, or other materials to represent rock layers. Build your model on wax paper. Include a "crack" down through the layers. Stack cubes on the top of the model to represent buildings and other surface features.
2. **Experiment** Find as many ways of moving the model as you can to show how the crust may move during an earthquake. What happens to the surface features as you move the model each way? Draw and describe each.

   Students might try shifting or sliding the model side to side, bouncing or bumping it up and down, and tilting it.

3. **Experiment** How can you show movement without causing any visible effect on the surface features?

   Possible answer: Slowly pull apart the bottom layers of clay.

### Drawing Conclusions

1. How many different ways could you move your model? How were they different?

   Possible answers: I moved the model three ways: up and down, sideways, or toward each other. The different movements went in different directions.

Name______________________________ Date____________



**2. Communicate** How did each way you moved the model affect the surface features? How did each way change the positions of the layers? Explain.

Each way the layers moved caused the surface features to move. When the model moved up, the layers were no longer lined up. When the model moved sideways, the layers tilted against each other. When the model folded, the layers appeared bent.

**3. Communicate** How did you move the model without moving the surface features? Did the model change in any way? Explain.

If the model is moved slightly, the surface features will not move. The model itself will change only slightly.

**4. Going Further: Experiment** How can you use your model to show how a mountain might rise up high above sea level? Explain and demonstrate.

Possible answer: Push two plates together to show bulging, or slide one plate over another.

## Inquiry

Think of your own questions that you might like to test. What other effects can you demonstrate with the clay model? (Sometimes enough pressure is created when plates collide that part of a plate melts.)

My Question Is:

Possible answer: How can I demonstrate a plate under pressure?

How Can I Test It:

Possible answer: I will push the plates toward each other and slide one plate over the other pushing down on the bottom plate.

My Results Are:

Possible answer: A plate is under great pressure when another plate slides on top of it.

Name_____________________ Date__________

Alternative Explore
Lesson 2

# Motion of the Crust

**Materials**

- newspapers
- scissors or ruler

## Procedure

1. Place a stack of newspapers 1 cm thick on a table.
2. Place your hands on the edges of the stack, and push toward the center of the paper. Observe how the paper moves. Record your observations.

   The paper bulges up at the center.

3. Cut several thicknesses of newspaper into two pieces, or tear them using a ruler as a straightedge. Then place the edges together again. Try to line up the lines of type. Move the two stacks in opposite directions. Record your observations.

   The lines of type do not match up.

4. Place the cut halves of paper on the desk, a few centimeters apart. Place your hands on the paper and quickly slide the two halves toward each other. Observe what happens. Record your observations.

   Parts of the two halves merge to form layers.

## Drawing Conclusions

Which way of moving the papers could be a model for how mountains are formed?

Pushing the edges of the stack toward the center.

Name ______________________ Date ____________

QUICK LAB

FOR SCHOOL OR HOME

Lesson 2

# Model of Earth

**Hypothesize** Can materials with different properties be used to make a solid Earth? Write a **Hypothesis:**

Possible hypothesis: A model of Earth can be made by selecting different materials to represent the layers in Earth.

## Materials

- mashed ripe banana (in a plastic bag)
- peanut butter
- hazelnut
- graham cracker crumbs (in a plastic bag)
- wax paper

## Procedure

**BE CAREFUL!** Students who are allergic to peanuts should not do this activity!

1. **Infer** You will use four materials to make a model of Earth on wax paper. Each material is one of Earth's layers. Read step 2. Decide which material represents which layer. Decide how thick each layer needs to be.
2. **Make a Model** Wash your hands. Cover a hazelnut with a layer of peanut butter. Put the covered nut in a plastic bag of mashed banana so that the banana covers it completely. Roll the result into graham cracker crumbs on wax paper.

## Drawing Conclusions

3. How does each material represent a different layer?

   Possible answer: There are four rock layers in Earth. Each layer has different properties. The inner core is solid, the outer core is liquid, the mantle is a solid that flows, and the crust is a thin solid layer of rock.

**4.** How thick did you decide to make each layer? Explain your reasoning.

Possible answer: The graham cracker crumb layer is the thinnest because it represents the crust, which is the thinnest layer. The banana layer is the thickest because it represents the mantle, which is the thickest layer.

**5.** **Going Further** Make a model of the plates in Earth's crust. Mix dirt and water together to make mud. Pour the mud on to a cookie sheet. Place the cookie sheet in the sun for several days to dry the mud. When the mud is completely dry, press on the outer edges. What happened to the dry mud when you pressed on it? How can this be related to Earth's crust?

When the edges of the mud are pressed on, the mud slab cracks into pieces. This simulates how Earth's crust may have been whole at into one time and how forces within the Earth may have broken the crust into pieces.

Can you relate this model to Earth's continents?

The shape of Earth's continents indicates that they may have been connected at one time.

Name________________________________ Date______________

**Explore Activity**
Lesson 3

# How Can You Identify a Mineral?

**Materials**

- mineral samples
- clear tape
- red marker
- copper penny or wire
- porcelain tile
- hand lens
- nail

**Hypothesize** How do you think people can tell minerals apart? Write a **Hypothesis**:

Possible hypothesis: Minerals can be identified by observing their properties and comparing the properties to those for known materials.

## Procedure

1. **Communicate** Use tape and a marker to label each sample with a number. On another sheet of paper, make a table with the column headings shown. Fill in the numbers under "Mineral" to match your samples.

   *Color = color of surface*

   *Porcelain Plate Test = the color you see when you rub the sample gently on porcelain*

   *Shiny Like a Metal = reflects light like a metal, such as aluminum foil or metal coins*

   *Scratch (Hardness) = Does it scratch copper? A nail?*

   *Other: Is it very dense? (Is a small piece heavy?) Has it got flat surfaces?*

| Mineral | Color | Shiny like a Metal (Yes/No) | Porcelain Plate Test | Scratch (Hardness) | Other |
|---|---|---|---|---|---|
| 1. | | | | | |
| 2. | | | | | |

2. **Observe** Use the table shown as a guide to collect data on each sample. Fill in the data in your table. Turn to the table on page 91 for more ideas to fill in "Other."

Name ____________________ Date __________

Explore Activity
Lesson 3

## Drawing Conclusions

1. Use your data and the table on the third page of this activity to identify your samples. Were you sure of all your samples? Explain.

   Identification may be difficult if some minerals have many of the same properties. Color is not reliable because a mineral can have different colors.

2. Which observations were most helpful? Explain.

   Possible answer: The porcelain test and hardness test were most useful because they gave the clearest results.

3. **Going Further: Experiment** How could you make a better scratch (hardness) test?

   Possible answer: Scratch a larger number of test materials with a wide range of known (relative) hardnesses.

**Inquiry**

Think of your own questions that you might like to test. Can minerals scratch each other?

My Question Is:

Possible answer: Can a mineral scratch other minerals that are less hard than it?

How I Can Test It:

Possible answer: I can try to use the hardest mineral to scratch the other minerals.

My Results Are:

Possible answer: Hard minerals can scratch softer minerals.

| PROPERTIES OF MINERALS | | | | | | |
|---|---|---|---|---|---|---|
| Mineral | Color(s) | Luster (Shiny as Metals) | Porcelain Plate Test (Streak) | Cleavage (Number) | Hardness (Tools Scratched by) | Density (Compared with Water) |
| Gypsum | colorless, gray, white, brown | no | white | varies | 2 (all six tools) | 2.3 |
| Quartz | colorless, various colors | no | none | no | 7 (streak plate) | 2.6 |
| Pyrite | brassy, yellow | yes | greenish black | no | 6 (steel file, streak plate) | 5.0 |
| Calcite | colorless, white, pale blue | no | colorless, white | yes—3 | 3 (all but fingernail) | 2.7 |
| Galena | steel gray | yes | gray to black | yes—3 (cubes) | 2.5 (all but fingernail) | 7.5 |
| Feldspar | gray, green yellow, white | no | colorless | yes—2 | 6 (steel file, streak plate) | 2.5 |
| Mica | colorless, silvery, black | no | white | yes—1 (thin sheets) | 2—3 (all but fingernail) | 3.0 |
| Hornblende | green to black | no | gray to white | yes—2 | 5–6 (steel file, streak plate) | 3.4 |
| Bauxite | gray, red brown, white | no | gray | no | 1–3 (all but fingernail) | 2.0–2.5 |
| Hematite | black, gray, red-brown | yes | red or red-brown | no | 1–6 (all) | 5.3 |

Name ______________________ Date ____________

Alternative Explore

Lesson 3

# Classifying Minerals

## Procedure

**Materials**

- samples of minerals
- poster board
- scale
- measuring cup
- water

1. Work with your group to develop ways to classify the mineral samples. You may classify them by color, feel, density, shape, or any other characteristics your group agrees on. List your group's suggestions.

   Answers will vary.

2. As a group, prepare a poster to describe your classification system. In the space below, sketch your ideas for the poster. Sketches will vary and should logically lay out each group system

## Drawing Conclusions

1. What characteristics did you use as a basis for your classification system?

   Answers will vary.

2. Did other groups use different characteristics? If so, describe them.

   Answers will vary.

3. After reviewing the posters of other groups, would you like to change your group's system? Explain.

   Explanations will vary but should state what students liked about another group's idea and how it improved on their own ideas.

Name ______________________ Date ____________

QUICK LAB

FOR SCHOOL OR HOME

Lesson 3

# Growing Crystals

**Hypothesize** How can you watch crystals grow?

Write a **Hypothesis**:

To grow crystals, dissolve salt in water and allow the water to evaporate.

## Materials

- foam cup half-filled with hot water
- granulated table salt
- 2 plastic spoons
- crystal of rock salt
- string (about 15 cm)
- pencil
- goggles

## Procedure

Your teacher will put a cup of hot water onto a counter for you.

**BE CAREFUL!** Wear goggles. Use a kitchen mitt if you need to hold or move the cup. Don't touch the hot water.

1. Use a plastic spoon to gradually add small amounts of salt to the water. Stir. Keep adding and stirring until no more will dissolve.
2. Tie one end of a 15-cm piece of string to a crystal of rock salt. Tie the other end to a pencil. Lay the pencil across the cup so that the crystal hangs in the hot salt water without touching the sides or bottom.
3. **Observe** Observe the setup for several days. Record what you see.

   Salt crystals deposit on the suspended crystal of rock salt.

## Drawing Conclusions

4. Did any crystals grow? If so, did they have many shapes or just one? Explain your answer. If not, how would you change what you did if you tried again?

Possible answer: Salt crystals grew on the suspended crystal. The crystals were the same shape. If crystals did not grow, review the procedure.

5. **Going Further** Grow needle-shaped crystals. Dissolve Epsom salt in water. Line a shallow dish with black construction paper so the crystals will be more visible. Place a very small amount of the solution in the dish. Set the dish where it will not be disturbed. Check the dish after one day for long needle-shaped crystals.

Name ______________________ Date ____________

**Explore Activity**
Lesson 4

# How Are Rocks Alike and Different?

**Materials**
- samples of rocks
- clear tape
- red marker
- hand lens
- copper wire
- streak plate
- balance
- metric ruler
- calculator

**Hypothesize** Are rocks all alike? Are they different? If so, how? Write a **Hypothesis**:

Possible hypothesis: Rocks are different in several ways, such as color, shape, and makeup.

## Procedure

1. Use the tape to number each sample in a group of rocks.
2. **Classify** Find a way to sort the group into smaller groups. Determine which properties you will use. Group the rocks that share one or more properties. Your fingernail, the copper wire, and the edge of a streak plate are tools you might use. Scratch gently. Record your results.

   Students might use properties such as color, luster, grain size, and layering. Results from scratching will vary depending on rocks.

3. **Use Numbers** You might estimate the density of each sample. Use a balance to find the mass. Use a metric ruler to estimate the length, width, and height. **Length x width x height = volume; Density = mass ÷ volume**

   Results will vary depending on rocks.

## Drawing Conclusions

1. How were you able to make smaller groups? Give supporting details from the notes you recorded.

   Students should discuss the properties they examined. Students may have grouped the rocks by color, hardness, size, pattern, or density.

2. Could you find more than one way to sort rocks into groups? Give examples of how rocks from two different smaller groups may have a property in common.

Rocks can be sorted in many ways. Different colored rocks might have the same hardness.

3. **Communicate** Share your results with others. Compare your systems for sorting the rocks.

Students will likely use different methods to sort the rocks.

4. **Going Further: Infer** How might a sample be useful based on the properties that you observed?

Possible answer: Hard rocks that are not brittle make good construction materials.

## Inquiry

Think of your own questions that you might like to test. How can you learn more about your rock samples?

My Question Is:

Possible answer: Can I learn more about rocks by magnifying my view of them?

How Can I Test It:

Possible answer: Observe each rock with a hand lens.

My Results Are

Possible answer: I can see different colors and smaller particles in the rocks.

Name ______________________ Date ____________

Alternative Explore

Lesson 4

# Display Types of Rocks

**Materials**

- rock samples
- hand lens
- art supplies
- poster board

## Procedure

1. Observe the rocks your teacher gave you. Use the hand lens to get a close look.
2. With your group, discuss ways that the rocks are alike and ways that they are different. Brainstorm ways to group the rocks by similarities. Record your group's ideas about grouping the rocks.

   Students may group the rocks by hardness, texture, color, or shine.

3. With your group, plan a display or poster to show how you grouped the rocks. Label each group to show the characteristics of the group.

## Drawing Conclusions

1. What characteristics did you choose to use as a basis for grouping the rocks?

   Answers will vary.

2. How did you show your decisions, with a poster or a display?

   Answers will vary.

3. Did other groups use different characteristics to group their rocks? Describe another group's system that you think was a good idea.

   Answers will vary.

Name ______________________ Date ____________

Process Skill Builder
Lesson 4

# Define Based on Observations

## Defining Soil

Earth's crust is made up of rocks and minerals. However, to get to the rocks, you usually have to dig through layers of soil.

Soil looks different at different places. It has different properties. Soil can be sandy. It can be moist.

Just what is soil? Make some observations. Write a definition that fits your observations.

### Materials

- moist soil sample in a plastic bag
- sand sample in a plastic bag
- hand lens
- 2 cups
- 2 plastic spoons

## Procedure

1. **Observe** Use a hand lens to examine a sample of moist soil. What materials can you find? How do their sizes compare? Write a description.

   Possible observations: Students should see different sized pieces of rock and bits of plant and animal matter.

2. Some soils are more like sand. How does a sample of sand compare with your moist soil sample?

   Possible answer: Sand is dry and has a more uniform appearance.

3. **Use Variables** Which sample absorbs water more quickly? Fill a cup halfway with sand and another with moist soil. Pour a spoonful of water in each at the same time.

   Possible answer: The water drains through the sand very quickly.

4. **Experiment** Which absorbs more water? Make a prediction. Find a way to test your prediction.

   Possible answer: Slowly add the same amount of water to small amounts of soil and sand until one is saturated. The soil will absorb more water.

5. **Experiment** Make any other observations. Look for other differences.

Possible answer: Sand looks like tiny rock pieces, while soil consists of a variety of materials. Soil holds together when pressed, sand does not.

## Drawing Conclusions

1. Based on your observations, what is soil made up of?

Possible answer: Soil is made of bits of rock and decaying plants and animals.

2. How may soils differ?

Possible answer: Different types of soil contain different types and proportions of rock and decaying animal and plant matter. This variation in composition results in different types of soil having different properties, such as water retention and drainage, nutrient content, and compactability.

3. **Define** Write a definition for *soil*. Take into account all your observations.

Possible answer: Soil is the product of rock erosion and the decay of plants and animals.

Name ______________________ Date __________

Explore Activity
Lesson 5

# What Makes Air Dirty?

**Hypothesize** What kinds of pollutants are in the air that can make it look as it does in the picture on the opening page of Lesson 5 of your textbook?

Write a **Hypothesis**:

Possible hypothesis: The air contains pollutants such as solid particles and gases.

## Materials

- 12 cardboard strips
- petroleum jelly
- plastic knife
- transparent tape
- string
- hand lens
- metric ruler
- marker

## Procedure

1. Make square "frames" by taping together the corners of four cardboard strips. Make three frames, and label them A, B, and C. Tie a 30-cm string to a corner of each frame.
2. Stretch and attach three strips of tape across each frame, with all sticky sides facing the same way. Use a plastic knife to spread a thin coat of petroleum jelly across each sticky side.
3. **Use Variables** Hang the frames in different places to try to collect pollutants. Decide on places indoors or outdoors. Be sure to tell a parent or teacher where.
4. **Observe** Observe each frame over four days. On a separate page, record the weather and air condition each day.
5. **Measure** Collect the frames. Observe the sticky sides with a hand lens and metric ruler to compare particles. Record your observations.

Students might use the metric ruler to measure the area of tape in order to calculate the number of particles per square centimeter. They may also measure large particles. Observations will vary.

Name _______________ Date _______________

**Explore Activity**
**Lesson 5**

## Drawing Conclusions

1. **Interpret Data** How did the frames change over time? How did the hand lens and ruler help you describe any pollution?

   Possible answer: Solid particles collected on the frames. The hand lens made viewing tiny particles possible. The ruler was used to measure the area of tape in order to calculate the number of particles per square centimeter, and in measuring large particles (millimeters).

2. **Communicate** Present your data in a graph to show differences in amounts. Use a separate piece of paper. Students might graph the number of particles per $cm^2$ vs. filter location, or particle size vs. number of particles for each location.

3. **Going Further: Use Variables** What kinds of pollutants would your frames not collect? How might you design a collector for them? How might you extend this activity over different periods of time?

   The frame did not collect gaseous pollutants. You might use a gas- tight container to collect gas samples for analysis. To extend the study, replace used frames and analyze them periodically.

**Inquiry**

Think of other questions that you might like to test. What type of particles do common air filters trap?

My Question Is:

Possible question: What particles do common air filters made of paper that fit over the mouth and nose (painter's masks) trap?

How I Can Test It:

Possible test: Hang some painter's masks in different locations for a period of time and later examine the filters with a hand lens.

My Results Are:

Possible answer: The filters may trap small solid particles.

Name________________________________ Date______________

Alternative Explore
Lesson 5

# Water Collector

## Procedure

1. Place a small amount of water in a container. Do not cover the container.
2. Place your container in a location where it won't be disturbed. Possible locations include a garden, the classroom, an office, or a room at home.
3. Leave the container in place until the water evaporates.
4. After the water has evaporated, examine the bottom of the container. What do you see?

   There will be some residue in the bottom of the container.

### Materials

- gallon containers
- water

## Drawing Conclusions

1. Where did you place your container?

   Answers will vary.

2. How long did it take for the water to evaporate?

   Answers will vary.

3. Observe your classmates' containers. Did all the containers contain the same type of material? Explain any differences you saw.

   Residue will depend on the source. Containers outside may contain soil and small, dried insects. Containers kept indoors may have some dust, especially if they were near something that makes dust, such as the classroom pencil sharpener.

4. Where did the material that you found in the container come from?

   The air

Name ______________________ Date ____________

QUICK LAB

FOR SCHOOL OR HOME

Lesson 5

# Acids

**Hypothesize** How can acid rain change a rock?

Write a **Hypothesis**:

Possible hypothesis: Acid rain can erode rocks by reacting with minerals in them such as limestone.

Your teacher will give you a stick of chalk and some rock samples.

## Materials

- chalk
- limestone and other rock samples
- vinegar (a mild acid)
- plastic cups
- goggles
- plastic wrap
- rubber bands
- plastic knife

## Procedure

**BE CAREFUL!** Wear goggles.

1. **Use Variables** Break a stick of chalk into smaller pieces. Place some small pieces in a plastic cup. Place each rock sample in its own cup. Slowly pour vinegar into each cup to cover each object.
2. Cover each cup using plastic wrap and a rubber band to help keep the vinegar from evaporating.
3. **Observe** Watch for any changes in the chalk and the rocks. Watch for several minutes and then at later times in the day. Record your observations.

   Students should see bubbles form on the chalk, on the limestone,and on some rocks. Students may notice weathering of the surfaces.

Name ______________________________ Date ______________

QUICK LAB

FOR SCHOOL OR HOME

Lesson 5

## Drawing Conclusions

4. Vinegar is a mild acid. How did it change the chalk?

   Possible answer: The acid reacted with limestone in the chalk. The surface of the chalk deteriorated and carbon dioxide gas was released.

5. Do all rocks change the same way? Explain based on your results.

   Possible answer: Not all rocks are weathered by acid rain. Different minerals in rock react with acids at different rates.

6. **Going Further** Acid rain causes metals to deteriorate more rapidly. This can be simulated using steel wool and vinegar. Write and conduct an experiment to simulate more rapid deterioration of metal by acid rain.

   My Hypothesis Is:

   Possible hypothesis: Acid rain deteriorates steel more rapidly than water deterioation steel.

   My Experiment Is:

   Obtain two pieces of steel wool, two plastic cups, vinegar, water, two small plastic plates, and a marking pen. Label one plate and one cup, "vinegar". Label the other plate and cup, "water". Place one piece of steel wool in each cup. Submerge one piece of steel wool in vinegar and the other in water. Drain both pieces of steel wool and place them on the proper plate. Check the steel wool pieces in one hour, then twice a day for several days. Record your observations.

   My Results Are:

   The steel wool soaked in vinegar rusted more quickly than the piece soaked in water.

Name ________________________ Date ____________

Explore Activity
Lesson 6

# Investigate How to Make Salt Water Usable

**Materials**

- tea bag
- deep pan
- plastic cup
- saucer (or petri dish)
- large, clear bowl or container
- water

**Hypothesize** How can water with something dissolved in it be changed into fresh water? Test your ideas.

Write a **Hypothesis:**

Possible hypothesis: Let the water evaporate and collect the clean water vapor.

## Procedure

1. **Make a Model** Keep a tea bag in a cup of water until the water is orange.
2. **Make a Model** Place a pan where there is strong light (sunlight, if possible). Pour some tea water into the saucer. Put the saucer in the pan. Cover the saucer with a large bowl.
3. **Observe** Look at the bowl and pan several times during the day and the next day. Note any water you see on the bowl or in the pan. Record your observations.

Possible answer: Clear water drops condense on the inside of the bowl and run or drip into the pan.

## Drawing Conclusions

1. How was the water that collected on the bowl and in the pan different from the tea water?

Possible answer: The water that collected is clear, not orange like the tea.

2. **Infer** What do you think caused the water to collect in the bowl and pan?

Possible answer: The water evaporated and condensed on the cool surfaces.

3. How does this model represent what might happen to salt water, the water of Earth's oceans?

Possible answer: Water evaporates from the oceans, leaving salt and other dissolved materials behind. The water vapor condenses in the cool atmosphere and returns as rain or snow.

4. **Use Variables** How long did it take for water to collect in the bowl and pan? How might this process be speeded up?

Possible answer: Heat the tea water and cool the bowl and pan to speed up the process.

5. **Going Further: Communicate** Do you think this model shows a useful way of turning ocean water into fresh water? Explain.

Possible answer: Yes, collecting water vapor is a good method of turning ocean water into fresh water.

## Inquiry

Think of your own questions that you might like to test. What other substances can your model remove from water?

My Question Is:

Possible question: Can this model remove sugar and food coloring from water?

How I Can Test It:

Possible test: Clean the experiment equipment. Dissolve sugar and food coloring in warm water. Place the solution in the saucer and rebuild the model.

My Results Are:

Possible answer: The condensed water was clear and did not taste sweet. The model removed the sugar and food coloring.

Name ____________________ Date __________

Alternative Explore
Lesson 6

# What's Left?

**Materials**

- saltwater solution
- hand lens
- heat source
- goggles
- pie pan

## Procedure

**BE CAREFUL!** Wear goggles.

1. Pour some saltwater solution into the pie pan.
2. Place the pie pan near a heat source, such as sunlight or a strong lamp.
3. Check the dish every hour to see if the water has evaporated.
4. When the water has evaporated, observe the material in the dish. Use a hand lens to get a closer look. Record your observations. Draw what you see through the magnifying lens in the space below.

There is a white residue, made up of fine crystals.

## Drawing Conclusions

1. What would be left if all the water in the oceans evaporated?

Salt and other dissolved substances would be left.

2. Why would it be useful to collect the water as it evaporates?

The water that evaporates and then condenses is fresh water.

It must be collected before it is lost to the air.

Name ______________________ Date __________

**Process Skill Builder**
Lesson 6

# Form a Hypothesis

**Materials**
- soil
- food color
- foam bits
- 2 aluminum pans
- water
- 2 textbooks

## How Do Wastes from Land Get into Lakes and Rivers?

In seeking an answer to a question, the first thing you might do is find out as much as possible. You make observations. You might look up information.

Next, you would think of an explanation for these observations. That explanation is a hypothesis. It may be stated as an "If . . . then" sentence. "If water runs over the land where garbage is dumped, then . . ." Sometimes you can test a hypothesis by making and observing a model.

## Procedure

1. **Hypothesize** Write a hypothesis to answer the question above.

   Possible answer: If water runs over the land where garbage is dumped, then the water will become polluted.

2. **Make a Model** Pack moist soil to fill one-half (one side) of one aluminum pan. As you pack the soil, add 10–20 drops of food color to the soil just below the surface. Sprinkle crumbled bits of foam over the top.
3. **Experiment** Use two books to tilt the pan with the soil side up. Place the lower edge of the soil-filled pan in the other pan. Pour water over the uppermost edge of the pan. Describe what happens. Let your model stand for some time, and observe it again.

   Possible answer: The water will pick up dirt and foam pieces, and dissolve the food coloring.

Name ________________________________ Date ____________

**Process Skill Builder**
Lesson 6

## Drawing Conclusions

1. How does this model represent wastes on land?

   Possible answer: The water represents groundwater and the soil represents land where garbage is dumped. The foam and food coloring simulate pollutants from dumped garbage. The foam represents surface trash and the food coloring represents chemicals.

2. Based on the model, how do wastes from land get into water? Does the model support your hypothesis? Explain.

   Possible answer: The groundwater that flows over the surface of the soil picks up trash. The groundwater that seeps into the soil dissolves and carries away chemicals. The model supported the hypothesis by simulating groundwater contamination from garbage dumps.

3. **Hypothesize** How can some wastes be removed from water? Form a hypothesis, and test your ideas.

   My Hypothesis Is:

   Possible hypothesis: To clean polluted water, pour it through a filter to remove solid waste.

   My Procedure Is:

   Possible procedure: Pour the dirty water through a filter to remove the foam pieces (and soil particles). Observe the water that flows through the filter.

   My Results Are:

   Possible result: The solid pollutants are trapped by the filter and the water that flows through the filter is cleaner.

Name ______________________ Date __________

Explore Activity
Lesson 7

# How Do Ocean and Fresh Water Compare?

**Hypothesize** How does the density of fresh water compare to the density of salt water? Test your ideas.

Write a **Hypothesis**:

Possible hypothesis: If fresh water is less dense than salt water, it will form layers when mixed with salt water.

## Materials

- 3 small plastic cups
- "ocean water"
- "fresh water"
- clear-plastic straw
- waterproof marking pen
- wax paper

## Procedure

1. Spread wax paper on your desk before you begin to work.
2. **Predict** What happens when you mix fresh and ocean water?

   Predictions may include that the salt and fresh water won't mix or that salt water will float on fresh water or visa the reverseversa.

3. **Experiment** From the bottom of the straw, make a mark every 4 cm. Gently place the bottom of the straw 4 cm under the surface of the "ocean water." Seal the top of the straw with your finger. With your finger still sealing the straw, lift it out of the water. Keeping your finger on top of the straw, place the bottom of the straw 8 cm down in the "fresh water." Lift your finger off the straw, then put it back again and lift the straw out of the water.
4. **Observe** What happened? Record the results. Now try it again, starting with "fresh water" first. Observe and record what happens.

   In both trials, water was drawn into the straw. When salt water is placed on top, it sinks and mixes with the freshwater drawn into the straw. When fresh water is on top, it forms a separate layer floating on the salt water drawn in.

Name______________________________ Date____________

Explore Activity
Lesson 7

## Drawing Conclusions

1. **Communicate** Which liquid combinations mixed in the straw and which made layers?

   When salt water is place on top, it sinks and mixes. When fresh water is on top, it forms colored layers.

2. **Going Further: Experiment** Make a third liquid by mixing equal parts of ocean water and fresh water. Experiment with the three liquids to see how many layers you can make.

   Possible answer: If you start with the fresh water, then add the mixed water, then add the salt water, you can get three layers.

**Inquiry**

Think of your own question that you might like to test. Will the layers created by adding fresh water on top of salt water stay separate indefinitely?

My Question Is:

Possible question: Will the layers created by adding fresh water on top of salt water stay separate indefinitely?

How I Can Test It:

Possible test: Leave the two layers together for a longer length of time. Record your observations.

My Results Are:

Possible answer: The fresh and the salt water will eventually mix.

Name________________________ Date____________

Alternative Explore
Lesson 7

# Salt Water Density

## Procedure

1. Pour the cupful of colored salt water into the fresh water along the side of the bowl.
2. Observe and record what happens.

   The salt water sinks beneath the fresh water.

3. Now reverse the experiment. Pour the cupful of colored fresh water into the salt water along the side of the bowl.
4. Observe and record what happens.

   The fresh water mixes near the top of the salt water.

## Materials

- water
- salt
- food coloring
- cup
- deep glass bowl
- teaspoon

## Drawing Conclusions

1. Which is denser, fresh water or salt water? Why?

   Salt water is denser. In the experiment, the salt water sank below the fresh water.

2. What do you think would happen if you mixed salt into the fresh water and repeated the experiment?

   The water in the cup and the water in the bowl would mix together.

3. How could the salt water be made even denser?

   You could add more salt to it.


Use with TE textbook page C83

Name ______________________ Date __________

QUICK LAB

FOR SCHOOL OR HOME

Lesson 7

# Salt Water and Fresh Water

**Hypothesize** How will salt water and fresh water differ in the way that they affect a floating object?

Write a **Hypothesis:**

Possible hypothesis: Objects will float more easily in salt water.

______________________________

## Materials

- jar
- pencil with eraser
- thumbtack
- "fresh water"
- "salt water"
- waterproof marker
- ruler

## Procedure

1. Fill a jar with fresh water to about 1 cm from the top. Carefully push a thumbtack into the center of the eraser of a pencil.
2. **Observe** Place the pencil, eraser side down, in the water. Let go. What happens?

   The pencil floats upward.

3. **Measure** Using a waterproof marker, mark the pencil to show where the water line is. Use a ruler to measure the length of the pencil above the water mark. Record this measurement.

   Measurements will vary.

   ______________________________

4. Fill the jar with salt water. Repeat steps 2–3.

Name ______________________ Date ____________

QUICK LAB
FOR SCHOOL OR HOME
Lesson 7

## Drawing Conclusions

**5.** How do your results for fresh water compare with your results for salt water?

The pencil floated higher in the salt water.

**6. Predict** What do you think will happen if you add a tablespoon of salt to your salt water? Test your prediction.

The more salt, the higher the pencil should float (until the water dissolves no more salt).

**7. Going Further** Would it be easier to swim in a freshwater lake or in a saltwater lake? Explain your answer.

Students should infer that it would be easier to swim in a saltwater lake because the salt water makes it easier to float.

Name ______________________ Date ____________

Explore Activity
Lesson 8

# How Do People Use Energy?

**Hypothesize** How many different ways do you use energy each day? How can you use less energy? Test your ideas.

Write a **Hypothesis:**

Possible hypothesis: I use energy by watching television, turning on lights, and riding in a car. I can use less energy by watching less

## Procedure

1. **Communicate** Make a list of all the different ways you use energy.

   Answers will vary. but may include cooking, heat or air conditioning transportation, lighting, TV, radio, CD player, computer, and so on.

2. Make a table listing all the kinds of energy you use in a day, how you use that energy, and how many hours you use each kind. Put your table on a separate sheet of paper.

## Drawing Conclusions

1. How many different ways do you use electricity each day? How many hours a day do you use electricity? What other sources of energy do you use? How many hours a day do you use each?

   Answers will vary. Other possible sources of energy: gasoline, natural gas, oil, wood, solar energy.

Name______________________________ Date__________

Explore Activity
Lesson 8

2. **Infer** Make a log to keep track of your energy use at home and at school. How can you use that information to help you make a plan to save energy?

Possible answer: Review the log to determine when energy is being wasted or how energy-consuming activities can be limited.

3. **Use Numbers** If it costs you an average of ten cents an hour for the energy you use, how much would the energy you use cost each week? About how much would it cost each month?

Weekly cost = average daily use (hrs/day) x 7 days/week x $.10 /hr.

Monthly cost = weekly cost x 4.3 weeks/month

4. **Going Further: Hypothesize** How can you use less electricity? How much money do you think you could save on energy in a month? How would you go about testing your hypothesis?

Possible Hypothesis: Conserve electricity by using lower wattage bulbs, turning off lights when not in use, taking quicker showers, and so on. Estimate the number of hours energy use will be reduced and calculate the savings. Test by keeping a log and calculating the actual savings.

**Inquiry**

Think of your own questions that you might like to test. Can you conserve energy by using less hot water?

My Question Is:

Possible question: Can I conserve by taking quicker showers?

How I Can Test It:

Possible test: Compare the average amount of energy used when taking long showers to the amount used when taking quick showers.

My Results Are:

Students might report that quicker showers save energy, because less energy is needed to heat a smaller volume of water.

Name ______________________ Date ____________

Alternative Explore

Lesson 8

# Pool the Data

**Materials**

- file cards
- chart paper
- marking pens

## Procedure

1. List the ways members of your group use energy, such as watching TV, burning gasoline in a car you ride in, burning a fuel to heat your home. Write each way you use energy on a separate card.
2. After you have listed all the uses, ask each member how much time each day he or she uses energy in that way.
3. If times of use vary a large amount from one group member to another, estimate an average time. Add the time to each card.
4. Arrange the cards in order of time used, from most to least.
5. Prepare a poster listing the ways your group uses energy and the times that each use lasts. List the uses in order of time used.

## Drawing Conclusions

1. What way does your group use energy for the longest time?

   Possible answer: Burning fuel to heat home

2. Did your group list heating the home as a 24-hour-per-day activity? Not all systems use energy constantly. Ask a family member to help you figure out how much of the time the system in your home actively uses energy to produce heat. How does this information change your results?

   Possible answer: My heating system does not use as much energy at night. This reduces our group's time for that activity.

3. Review the ways you use energy. Which ones would you be willing to cut down on in an effort to save energy?

   Possible answer: Watching television

Name ______________________ Date ____________

QUICK LAB

FOR SCHOOL OR HOME

Lesson 8

# Fuel Supply

**Hypothesize** We are using fossil fuels at the rates shown in the table. How long will Earth's fossil fuel supply last? Write a **Hypothesis:**

Possible hypothesis: Oil and natural gas supplies will last another 100 years.

## Procedure

This table shows how fast we are using up oil and natural gas.

| WORLD SUPPLY OF OIL AND NATURAL GAS (as of January 1, 1996) | |
|---|---|
| Oil | 1,007 billion barrels (1,007,000,000,000) |
| Natural gas | 4,900 trillion cubic feet |
| **WORLD USE OF OIL AND NATURAL GAS FOR 1995** | |
| Oil | about 70 million barrels a day (70,000,000) |
| Natural gas | about 78 trillion cubic feet |

1. **Observe** Examine the data in the table.
2. **Communicate** Draw a graph in the space below showing how long the fossil fuels we know about will last, based on the data in the table.

   Years of oil = 1,007 billion barrels ÷ 70 million barrel/day ÷ 365 days/year = 39 years; oil will be depleted in the year 2035 (1996 + 39 yrs). Years of gas = 4,900 trillion cubic feet ÷ 78 trillion cubic feet/year = 63 years; gas will be depleted in the year 2059 (1996 + 63 years).

## Drawing Conclusions

3. **Infer** How long will it be until we run out of each type of fossil fuel? Assume that the rate of use remains the same.

   Extrapolate the graphs to find the year each fuel will be depleted.

4. **Going Further** Sources of energy other than fossil fuels are becoming more common. Write and conduct an experiment to learn about usage of alternative energy sources.

   My Hypothesis Is:

   Possible hypothesis: What are the most common alternative energy sources in the world today?

   My Experiment Is:

   Possible experiment: Use research materials to learn about and compare usage of alternative energy sources.

   My Results Are:

   Possible results: Water, wind, and the Sun are the most common alternative energy sources.

Name ______________________ Date ____________

Explore Activity
Lesson 1

# Does the Sun's Angle Matter?

**Hypothesize** How does the angle at which the Sun's energy hits Earth affect the warming of Earth? Write a **Hypothesis:**

Possible hypothesis: The more directly sunlight hits Earth, the warmer Earth gets.

## Materials

- 3 thermometers
- centimeter ruler
- stopwatch
- triangular blocks
- scissors
- foam bowl
- black paper
- tape
- clay
- white paper
- 150-W clear-bulb lamp

## Procedure

**BE CAREFUL!** Do not look into the lamplight. Prop up a foam bowl, using a plate or clay, to shield your eyes from the light.

1. Place a thermometer onto each of the three blocks, as shown. Cover each with black paper. Put blocks 20 cm from the light bulb, level with its filament (curly wire).

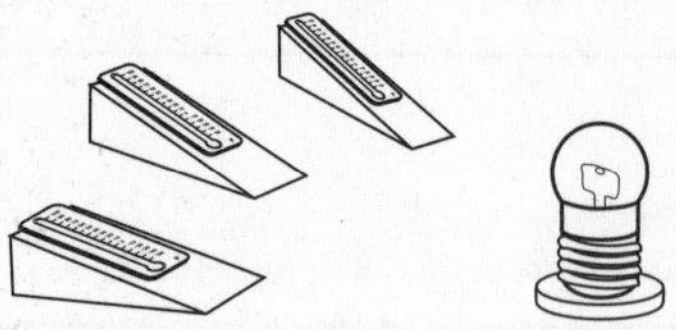

2. **Observe** Measure the starting temperature at each block. Record the temperatures.

   Answers will vary.

3. **Predict** What will happen when the lamp is turned on? Turn the lamp on. Record the temperature at each block every two minutes for ten minutes, in a data table on another sheet of paper.

   Students might predict that when the light is turned on, the temperature at the surface of the blocks will increase.

4. **Communicate** On another sheet of paper, make a line graph showing the change in temperature at each block over time.

   Graphs should have "Time (mins)" as x-axis and "Temperature" as y-axis. The line associated with each block will be different.

5. **Use Variables** Repeat the activity with white paper.

Name ______________________ Date ____________

Explore Activity

Lesson 1

## Drawing Conclusions

1. **Communicate** Which block's surface was warmed most by the lamplight? Which block's surface was warmed the least?

   The surface of the block that received the most direct light was warmed the most. The block that received the least direct light was warmed the least.

2. **Infer** How does the angle at which light hits a surface affect how much the surface is heated? How does the surface color affect how much it is heated?

   The more directly the Sun hits the surface, the more the surface is warmed. Students should infer that darker colors absorb more sunlight, warming the surface more.

3. **Going Further: Experiment** What other factors might affect how much a surface is warmed by sunlight? How would you test your ideas?

   Possible answers might include how rough or smooth the surface is; how dull or shiny it is; what type of material it is made of. Accept any reasonable ideas.

**Inquiry**

Think of your own questions that you might like to test. What other factors might affect temperature on different parts of Earth?

My Question Is:

Possible question: Does the time of year affect temperature?

How I Can Test It:

I can find and compare the temperatures for September and December.

My Results Are:

Possible answer: Temperatures change with the seasons.

Name________________________________ Date______________

Alternative Explore

Lesson 1

# Cold at the Poles

## Procedure

**Materials**

- globe
- flashlight

1. Darken the classroom by shutting off the lights and closing the blinds.
2. Place a globe on your desk.
3. Holding a flashlight, stand one or two paces from the globe.
4. Turn on the flashlight and shine it onto the globe.
5. Hold the flashlight level with the equator. Observe how the light strikes the equator and record your observations.

   The light strikes the equator perpendicular to it or straight on, so it looks bright.

6. **Observe** How does the light strike the north and south poles? Record your observations.

   The light strikes the poles at an angle, so it does not look very bright.

## Drawing Conclusions

1. What do the globe and flashlight represent?

   The globe represents Earth and the flashlight represents the Sun.

2. **Compare and Contrast** How does sunlight strike Earth at the equator and at the poles?

   It strikes at different angles, hitting perpendicular at the equator and at an angle at the poles.

3. Why do you think temperatures near the equator are warmer than those near the poles?

   At the equator, the angle at which sunlight strikes causes the light to be more intense and the surface to get warmer.

Name ______________________ Date ____________

QUICK LAB
FOR SCHOOL OR HOME
Lesson 1

# Investigating Angles

**Hypothesize** Why does the angle of insolation cause a difference in warming? Write a **Hypothesis:**

Possible hypothesis: The angle of insolation determines how much direct sunlight a location receives: the greater the angle of insolation, the warmer it is; the smaller the angle of insolation, the colder it is because the Sun's rays are more spread out.

## Materials

- flashlight
- modeling clay
- 3 toothpicks
- sheet of graph paper
- ruler

## Procedure

1. Fold a sheet of graph paper lengthwise in three equal parts. Put a small lump of clay in the middle of each part. Stand a toothpick straight up in each lump of clay.
2. Hold a flashlight directly over the first toothpick. Have a partner trace a line around the circle of light and trace the toothpick shadow.
3. **Use Variables** Repeat step 2 for the other two toothpicks, changing only the angle of the flashlight. Keep distance of flashlight constant.
4. **Measure** Count the number of boxes in each circle. Measure the lengths of the toothpick shadows. Record your results in the table below.

| Toothpick | Number of Boxes | Length of Shadow |
|---|---|---|
| 1 | | |
| 2 | | |
| 3 | | |

The number of boxes should increase as the angle is decreased. The lengths of the toothpick shadows should increase as the angle is decreased.

Name______________________ Date____________

QUICK LAB
FOR SCHOOL OR HOME
Lesson 1

## Drawing Conclusions

5. **Infer** How is the length of the shadows related to the angle?

When the Sun is directly overhead (at a 90° angle), its shadow is shortest. As the angle decreases, the shadow lengthens.

6. **Infer** How is the number of boxes in the circle related to the angle?

When the light is overhead, the light covers the fewest number of squares. As the angle decreases, the light covers more boxes.

7. **Going Further** How does the angle of insolation affect where you live? Compare and contrast the local climate with the climate at the equator and at Earth's poles. Write and conduct an experiment.

My Hypothesis Is:

Answers will vary based on location of residency. Possible hypothesis: It is cooler where I live than it is at the equator, but warmer than it is at Earth's poles.

My Experiment Is:

Possible experiment: Place a flashlight 20 cm from a globe. The flashlight should be directed at the equator. Using a pencil, have your partner draw the outline the flashlight makes on the globe. Compare the angle of insolation at the equator, the poles, and where you live.

My Results Are:

Possible answer: The angle of insolation is greater at the equator than where I live, so it's warmer at the equator. The angle of insolation is smaller at the poles than where I live, so it's colder at the poles.

Name ______________________ Date ____________

Explore Activity
Lesson 2

# Where Does the Puddle Come From?

**Materials**

- plastic cups
- ice
- paper towels
- food coloring
- thermometer
- goggles

**Hypothesize** Think about putting a cold glass of lemonade on a table on a hot, humid day. Moisture forms on the side of the glass and in a puddle around the bottom. Where does the moisture come from? How might you design an experiment to test your ideas? Write a **Hypothesis:**

Possible hypothesis: Students might hypothesize that the water comes from the air.

## Procedure: Design Your Own

**BE CAREFUL!** Wear goggles.

1. **Form a Hypothesis** At the top of this page, write down your idea about why a puddle forms around a frosty drink. Where do you think the puddle came from? Answers will vary.
2. **Experiment** Describe what you would do to test your idea. How would your test support or reject your idea?

   Students might describe placing ice and tinted water into a cup, adding a straw, marking the water level on the straw, measuring and recording the temperature of the water and the air at intervals, and comparing the conditions when water droplets form with those at the beginning of the experiment.

3. **Communicate** On another sheet of paper draw a diagram showing how you would use the materials. Keep a record of your observations.
   Suggest to students that they organize their data in a chart.

## Drawing Conclusions

1. **Communicate** Describe the results of your investigation.

   The water level inside the glass does not go down, and the water droplets on the side of the glass are not tinted.

2. **Communicate** What evidence did you gather? Explain what happened.

   Answers will vary, but might include that the temperature of the water increased, the temperature of the air decreased, untinted water droplets formed, and the water level in the cup did not change.

**3. Infer** How does this evidence support or reject your explanation?

The fact that the water droplets did not come from inside the cup supports the hypothesis that the water comes from the air.

**4. Going Further: Use Variables** Do you get the same results on a cool day as on a warm day? Do you get the same results on a humid day as on a dry day? How might you test your ideas?

On a cool day, less water will form on the glass. More water will form on the glass on a humid day because condensation is greater than evaporation. Students might cool the area with a fan or place the set-up in the refrigerator, then repeat the experiment on a day when the local humidity is higher.

**Inquiry**

Think of your own questions that you might like to test. How might temperature affect the results of this experiment?

My Question Is:

Possible answer: What happens when a container holding a hot liquid is placed in cool surroundings?

How I Can Test It:

Possible answer: I can repeat the experiment by putting a cup of hot water in the refrigerator.

My Results Are:

Possible answer: Water does not form in a puddle around the container.

Name ______________________ Date ____________

Alternative Explore

Lesson 2

# Where'd It Go?

**Materials**

- two jars, one with a lid
- wax pencil
- water

## Procedure

1. Pour an equal amount of water into each of the jars.
2. Tightly screw the lid onto one of the jars.
3. With a wax pencil, mark the level of water in each jar.
4. Leave the jars where they will be undisturbed overnight.
5. The next day, observe the water level in each jar and record your observations.

   The water level in the open jar dropped. That of the closed jar dropped slightly at first and then leveled off.

6. Record any other observations you made.

   The closed jar may have condensation on its sides.

## Drawing Conclusions

1. What do you think happened to the water in the open jar?

   Some of it moved into the air by evaporation.

2. Did you observe the same results in both jars? Explain why or why not.

   In the open jar, evaporation from the water was greater than condensation back into the water, so the water level dropped. In the closed jar, condensation increased until it equaled evaporation, at which point the water level remained the same.

Name ______________________ Date ____________

QUICK LAB

FOR SCHOOL OR HOME

Lesson 2

# Transpiration

**Hypothesize** What evidence can you find for transpiration?

Write a **Hypothesis:**

Possible hypothesis: Students might hypothesize that the plastic bag will trap evidence of transpiration.

## Materials

- potted houseplant (geraniums work well)
- transparent plastic bag

## Procedure

1. Place a clear-plastic bag completely over a houseplant. Tie the bag tightly around the base of the stem. Do not put the soil-filled pot into the bag.
2. **Observe** Place the plant in a sunny location. Observe it several times a day. When you are done, remove the plastic bag from the plant.

   Students will observe moisture forming in the bag.

## Drawing Conclusions

3. **Communicate** Describe what you see on the inside of the bag. How can you explain what happened?

   Water droplets form on the inside of the bag as a result of transpiration. The plant absorbs water through its roots, then gives off water through its leaves.

4. **Draw Conclusions** *Transpiration* sounds like *perspiration*—sweating. How might the two processes be alike?

   Both transpiration and perspiration are processes where water is given off.

5. **Predict** How would your results vary if you put the plant in the shade?

   There would be less transpiration.

6. **Going Further** How do you think temperature might affect transpiration? How would you set up a test?

My Hypothesis Is:

Possible hypothesis: The rate of transpiration is directly proportional to temperature. As temperature rises, the rate of transpiration increases.

My Experiment Is:

Possible experiment: Repeat the above experiment with two plants, one placed in a cool location and one placed in a hot location.

My Results Are:

Possible answer: Students will find that more transpiration occurs in the plant in the hot location.

Name ______________________________ Date ____________

Explore Activity
Lesson 3

# How Do Clouds Form?

**Hypothesize** Sometimes the sky is full of clouds. Sometimes there are no clouds at all. Why? What makes a cloud form? What do evaporation and condensation have to do with it? Write a **Hypothesis:**

Possible hypothesis: Students might hypothesize that clouds form from condensing water vapor.

## Materials

- hot tap water
- 2 identical clear containers
- mug
- 3 ice cubes
- food coloring

Watch what can happen when you cool off some air.

## Procedure

**BE CAREFUL!** Be careful handling the hot water.

1. Chill container 1 by putting it in a refrigerator or on ice for about ten minutes.
2. Fill a mug with hot water.
3. **Make a Model** Fill container 2 with hot water. Place empty cold container 1 upside down on top of container 2 with the water. Fit the mouths together carefully. Place the ice cubes on top of container 1.
4. **Observe** Record your observations on another sheet of paper.

## Drawing Conclusions

1. **Communicate** What did you observe?

   A mist (or fog) and some droplets of water formed.

2. **Communicate** Where did this take place?

   Inside the top container.

Name ______________________ Date ____________

**Explore Activity**
**Lesson 3**

**3. Infer** Where did the water come from? Explain what made it happen.

The water evaporated from the hot water into the air. Then as the surrounding air was cooled, some of the water vapor in the air condensed. Students might infer that the cold upper container cooled the air containing water vapor rising from below. As it cooled, the water condensed, forming droplets and a "cloud."

**4. Go Further: Infer** Where would you expect to find more clouds—over the ocean or over a desert? Why?

Clouds form from condensing water vapor. You could expect more clouds over an ocean, where more water would evaporate into the air, than over a desert, where there is little water to evaporate into the air.

## Inquiry

Think of your own questions that you might like to test. Do dry conditions affect clouds?

My Question Is:

Possible answer: Does the water in clouds evaporate?

How I Can Test It:

Possible answer: Repeat the experiment, then replace the bottom container with an empty, dry container to simulate dry conditions.

My Results Are:

Possible answer: The moisture (cloud) in the top container will evaporate.

Name ______________________ Date ____________

Alternative Explore
Lesson 3

# Make a Cloud

## Procedure

**BE CAREFUL!** Keep away from the tea kettle spout and steam to avoid getting burned. Wait until the tea kettle cools before handling it.

**Materials**

- electric tea kettle
- water
- metal pie plate
- tongs
- oven mitt

1. Fill the tea kettle about half way with water.
2. Plug in the tea kettle, turn it on (if necessary), and wait for the water to start boiling.
3. **Observe** Observe the spout of the tea kettle and record your observations.

   Teachers should do this as a demonstration as students watch from a safe distance. Steam can cause burns! Steam or water droplets form above the spout.

4. Use the mitt and tongs to hold the metal pie plate above the spout.
5. **Observe** Observe what happens and record your observations.

   Many tiny water droplets form on the underside of the metal pie plate where the steam hits it.

6. Turn off and unplug the tea kettle

## Drawing Conclusions

1. What happened when the water in the kettle boiled? Explain your observations.

   Liquid water in the kettle evaporated and moved into the air and out of the spout. As the warm water vapor rose, it cooled and formed steam, or tiny water droplets, in the air.

2. When you held up the pie pan, where did a "cloud" form? Why did it form there?

   A "cloud" of tiny water droplets formed where the steam hit the pie pan. As warm water in the air rose from the spout, it hit the colder metal surface, cooled, and condensed.

Name ______________________ Date ____________

QUICK LAB

FOR SCHOOL OR HOME

Lesson 3

# Feel the Humidity

**Hypothesize** Why do you feel warmer on a high humidity day? Write a **Hypothesis:**

Possible hypothesis: Students might hypothesize that on a humid day sweat cannot evaporate as effectively.

## Materials

- 5-cm-square piece of old cotton cloth
- rubber band
- thermometer
- 1 c of warm water
- $\frac{1}{2}$ c of cold water

## Procedure

**BE CAREFUL!** Be careful handling warm water.

1. **Observe** Use a thermometer to record the air temperature.

   Answers will vary.

2. Put the thermometer in cold water. Slowly add warm water until the water temperature matches the air temperature.
3. Wrap a 5-cm-square piece of old cotton cloth around the bulb of the thermometer. Gently hold it with a rubber band. Dampen the cloth in the water.
4. **Observe** Gently wave the thermometer in the air. Record temperatures every 30 seconds for 3 minutes in the table below.

| Time | Temperature |
|---|---|
| 30 seconds | |
| 1 minute | |
| 1 minute, 30 seconds | |
| 2 minutes | |
| 2 minutes, 30 seconds | |
| 3 minutes | |

Name ______________________ Date ______________

QUICK LAB
FOR SCHOOL OR HOME
Lesson 3

## Drawing Conclusions

**5. Infer** What happened to the temperature of the wet cloth? How does the cloth feel? Explain.

The temperature of the wet cloth drops. When the cloth is touched, it feels cool.

**6. Infer** If you try this experiment on a day that is humid and on a day that is dry will you get the same results? Explain.

The difference between the two temperatures would be greater on a dry day than on a humid day, because more of the moisture would evaporate and cool the thermometer on a dry day.

**7. Going Further** In a school track meet, would sweating cool the runners more on a humid day or on a dry day? Write and conduct an experiment.

My Hypothesis Is:

Possible hypothesis: Sweat evaporates faster on dry days than on humid days, so sweating would cool the runners more on a dry day.

My Experiment Is:

Possible experiment: Run either a quarter of a mile or until you sweat on a humid day. Repeat on a dry day.

My Results Are:

Possible answer: Sweat will evaporate more on a dry day, so there will be a greater cooling effect.

Name ______________________ Date __________

Explore Activity

Lesson 4

# What Can Change Air Pressure?

**Hypothesize** Air moves from one place to another because of differences in air pressure. What causes these differences? Make a model to test your ideas. Write a **Hypothesis:**

Possible hypothesis: Students might hypothesize that air pressure changes when conditions in the atmosphere change.

## Materials

- plastic jar with hole in bottom
- plastic sandwich bag
- rubber band
- masking tape

## Procedure

1. **Make a Model** Set up a jar-and-bag system as shown. Make sure the masking tape covers the hole in the jar. Have a partner place both hands on the jar and hold it firmly. Reach in and slowly pull up on the bottom of the bag. Describe what happens.

Step 1

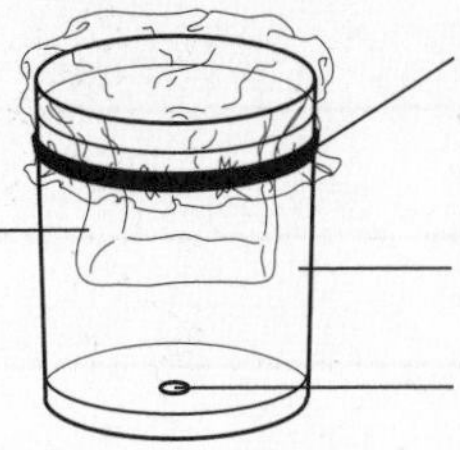


The bag cannot be pulled up.

2. **Experiment** Pull the small piece of tape off the hole in the bottom of the jar. Repeat step 1. Push in on the bag. Record your results.

The bag can be pulled up. When the bag is pushed in, air moves out of the hole.

3. **Observe** Place some small bits of paper on the table. Hold the jar close to the table. Point the hole toward the bits of paper. Pull up on the bag, and observe and record what happens.

The bits of paper are drawn to the hole.

4. **Experiment** Do just the opposite. Push the bag back into the jar. What happened?

The paper bits are blown away by the air leaving the jar.

Name______________________________ Date____________

Explore Activity
Lesson 4

## Drawing Conclusions

1. **Observe** What differences did you observe with the hole taped and with the tape removed?

When the hole was taped, air pressure inside the bag kept the bag from being pulled out of the jar. When the tape was removed, air was able to move into the jar.

2. **Infer** Explain what happened each time you pushed the bag back into the jar. How does this model show air pressure changes?

When the bag was pushed into the jar, air was pushed out of the bottom of the jar. The air was being squeezed into a smaller space so it escaped out the hole. The model shows that volume affects air pressure. When more space is available, pressure is lower, but when air is confined in a smaller volume, air pressure increases.

3. **Going Further: Use Variables** Will the model work the same with paper clips? Bits of cotton? Make a prediction, and test it.

Possible prediction: Some materials will be blown by air leaving jar.

**Inquiry**

Think of your own questions that you might like to test. Does air temperature affect air pressure?

My Question Is:

Possible answer: How will warm air affect the results of the experiment?

How I Can Test It:

Possible answer: Repeat the experiment after leaving the jar-and-bag system in the Sun to warm the air inside the jar.

My Results Are:

Possible answer: Warm air has lower pressure than cold air.

Name ______________________ Date ____________

Alternative Explore
Lesson 4

# Pushing Air

**Materials**
- large suction cup

## Procedure

1. Place the open end of the large suction cup against the chalkboard.
2. Push the stick attached to the cup as far as you can toward the chalkboard. Observe what happens and record your observations.

   The cup collapses and air may be heard rushing out of the suction cup.

3. Let go of the stick. Observe what happens and record your observations.

   The stick springs back and the suction cup sticks to the chalkboard.

## Drawing Conclusions

1. What happened to the air inside the suction cup when you pushed the stick in?

   It was forced out of the cup.

2. How did the pressure of the air inside the suction cup change after you pushed in and released the stick? Explain your answer.

   Pushing the stick forces air out of the suction cup, so that the same volume contains less air. As a result, the air pressure inside the suction cup is decreased.

3. Explain what happened to the suction cup after you let go of the stick.

   The suction cup sticks to the chalkboard because the air outside the cup has greater pressure than the air inside the cup and pushes on it, holding it in place.

Name ______________________ Date ____________

**Process Skill Builder**

**Lesson 4**

# Interpret Data

## A Weather Station Model

A weather station model includes temperature, cloud cover, air pressure, pressure tendency, wind speed, and wind direction. The circle is at the location of the station. You will interpret the data—use the information—from the weather use station models to answer questions and solve problems.

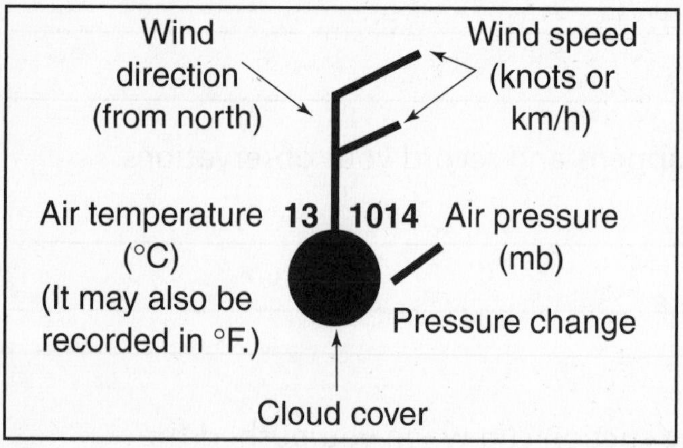


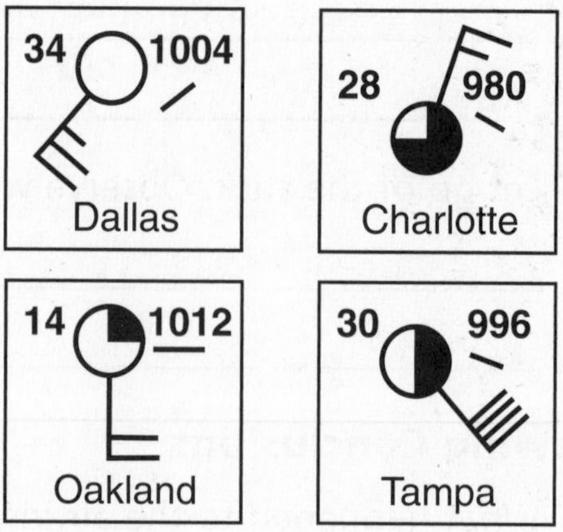


## Procedure

1. **Use Numbers** Look carefully at the Dallas weather station model. How fast is the wind blowing? What is the wind direction? Record your answers.

   Wind speed: 33–57 km/h (19–31 knots); wind direction: from southwest
   ______________________________________________

2. **Interpret Data** What other information does this weather station model give you?

   Amount of cloud cover, air temperature, and air pressure
   ______________________________________________

   ______________________________________________

3. Look at the other weather station models. On the next page, make a table recording weather conditions for each city.

   Remind students that tables consist of columns and rows, with space for appropriate headings. They should construct a 6-column by 5-row chart with the following column labels: city, wind speed, wind direction, cloud cover, temperature, and pressure.

Name ______________________ Date __________

**Process Skill Builder**

Lesson 4

## Drawing Conlusions

1. Compare the information in the table you made with these station models. Which way is the information easier to interpret?

   Answers will vary depending on students' preferences.

2. **Interpret Data** Where was wind fastest? Slowest? Which tells you this information more quickly, the table or the models?

   Wind was fastest in Tampa, and slowest in Charlotte. Students may interpret the information in either format more quickly.

3. **Communicate** Compare and contrast other weather conditions in the cities.

   Charlotte had the most cloud cover, while Dallas had the least.
   Oakland had the lowest temperature, while Dallas had the highest.
   Air pressure was highest in Oakland and lowest in Charlotte.

| City | Wind Speed | Wind Direction | Cloud Cover | Temperature | Air Pressure (mb) |
|---|---|---|---|---|---|
| Dallas | 33–57 km/h | southwest | clear | 34°C | 1004 |
| Oakland | 28–44 km/h | south | scattered clouds | 14°C | 1012 |
| Charlotte | 19–35 km/h | northeast | mostly cloudy | 28°C | 980 |
| Tampa | 56–88 km/h | southeast | partly cloudy | 30°C | 996 |

Name ______________________ Date ____________

Explore Activity
Lesson 5

# How Can You Compare Weather?

**Hypothesize** How can you tell where the weather may change? Test your ideas. How would you use a weather map to give a weather report of the country? Write a **Hypothesis:**

Possible hypothesis: Students might hypothesize that a national weather map indicates present and future weather patterns.

## Materials

- station model key
- newspaper weather map (optional)
- pencil
- crayons

## Procedure

**Communicate** Think of the country in large regions—the Northeast, the Southwest, and so on. Think of regions like the Pacific Coast, the Atlantic Coast, and the Gulf Coast. Write a report for the weather in each region based on the map you see on page 142. Use another sheet of paper if necessary.

Northeast, cold, cloudy, and rainy; Southeast, warm; North central, cold; South central, cool; Northwest, cool and partly cloudy; Southwest, warm and clear

Name ____________________ Date ____________

**Explore Activity**
Lesson 5

## Drawing Conclusions

1. **Infer** Which areas are having warm, rainy weather?

   New Orleans, Galveston, Cincinnati

2. **Infer** Where is the weather cool and dry?

   Answers include the Northwest; parts of the midwest.

3. **Predict** How do you think weather in any part of the country may change, based on the data in this map? Give reasons for your answer. How would you check your predictions?

   Since weather fronts move from west to east, the eastern border might experience some dry, cool weather in the future. Students can study a current map, make additional predictions and check them by studying national weather maps each day for a week.

4. **Going Further: Interpret Data** Using weather maps in a newspaper or the one on page D53 of your textbook, describe the weather.

   Answers will vary.

**Inquiry**

Think of your own questions that you might like to test. Can temperatures vary within a small area?

My Question Is:

Possible answer: Can cities that are close together have significantly different temperatures?

How I Can Test It:

Possible answer: I can study a regional weather map to compare and contrast weather conditions.

My Results Are:

Possible answer: Temperatures can vary greatly within a small region.

Name____________________ Date__________

**Explore Activity**
**Lesson 5**

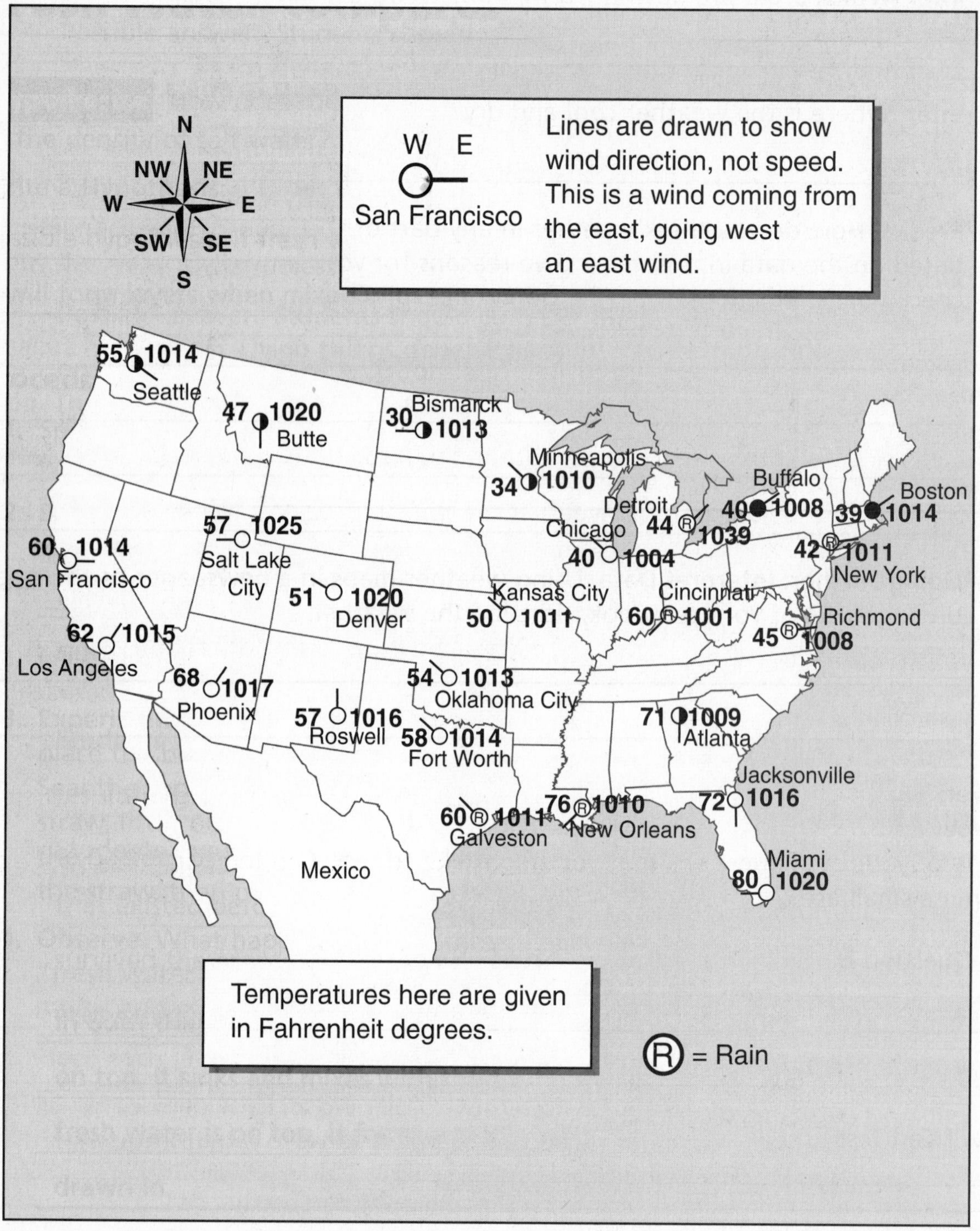
N
NW
NE
W
E
SW
SE
S
W E
San Francisco
Lines are drawn to show wind direction, not speed. This is a wind coming from the east, going west an east wind.
55 1014 Seattle
47 1020 Butte
30 Bismarck 1013
34 Minneapolis 1010
57 1025 Salt Lake City
60 1014 San Francisco
51 1020 Denver
62 1015 Los Angeles
68 1017 Phoenix
57 1016 Roswell
54 1013 Oklahoma City
58 1014 Fort Worth
50 1011 Kansas City
40 1004 Chicago
44 R 1039 Detroit
60 R 1001 Cincinnati
40 1008 Buffalo
39 1014 Boston
42 R 1011 New York
45 R 1008 Richmond
71 1009 Atlanta
72 1016 Jacksonville
80 1020 Miami
76 R 1010 New Orleans
60 R 1011 Galveston
Mexico
Temperatures here are given in Fahrenheit degrees.
R = Rain

Name ______________________ Date ____________

Alternative Explore

Lesson 5

# On the Table

## Procedure

**Materials**

- weather map on page 142
- newspaper weather map (optional)
- station model key

1. **Examine** Study the weather map on page 142 or a newspaper weather map. Think of the country in large regions—the Northeast, the Southwest, and so on. Think of regions like the Pacific Coast, the Atlantic Coast, and the Gulf Coast, in which you could group the weather data shown. List the regions you will use to group the weather data.

   Possible regions include Northeast, Mid Atlantic, Southeast, North Central, South Central, Pacific Coast, Atlantic Coast, Gulf Coast.

2. **Organize** Record the data on the weather map in the table below. Be sure to group data from a single region together in the table. Continue the table on a separate sheet of paper.

| Region | City | Temperature (°F) | Air Pressure (mb) | Wind Direction | Cloud Cover |
|---|---|---|---|---|---|
| | | | | | |
| | | | | | |
| | | | | | |
| | | | | | |
| | | | | | |

## Drawing Conclusions

1. In which regions is the weather warm and rainy? Cold and dry?

   For map on p. 55: answers include warm and rainy areas: New Orleans, Galveston, Cincinnati. Cold and dry areas: Bismarck, Minneapolis, Chicago

2. How did the table help you to recognize regional weather patterns?

   Organizing the data into regions on a table made it easy to spot similar weather data at nearby stations and thus regional weather patterns.

Name ______________________________ Date ______________

QUICK LAB

FOR SCHOOL OR HOME

Lesson 5

# Weather Prediction

**Hypothesize** How can you use a weather map to predict the weather? Write a **Hypothesis:**

Possible hypothesis: Students might hypothesize that symbols on weather maps help scientists evaluate and predict the movement of weather systems.

## Procedure

1. The map on page 146 shows weather in the United States at 6 P.M. on October 29. Describe the weather in Washington, D.C. The temperatures are in degrees Celsius.

   The temperature is 7° Celsius and it is breezy.

2. **Analyze** Describe the weather in the northwest part of the country and in the southeast.

   In the northwest and most of the southeast, it is breezy with patches of clouds and temperatures in the single digits. In Florida, it is breezy and cloudy, with temperatures in the 20s.

Name ______________________ Date ____________

QUICK LAB

FOR SCHOOL OR HOME

Lesson 5

## Drawing Conclusions

**3. Infer** Weather patterns move from west to east across the United States. How do you think the weather just east of the cold front will change in the next day or so? Explain.

Temperatures behind the cold front are cooler than those in front of the cold front, so weather just east of the cold front should get cooler in the next day or so.

**4. Going Further** Why do you think forecasting the weather is important?

Possible answer: Weather forecasting allows area residents advance warning about changes in the weather, so that they can prepare for severe weather conditions, such as hurricanes and tornadoes.

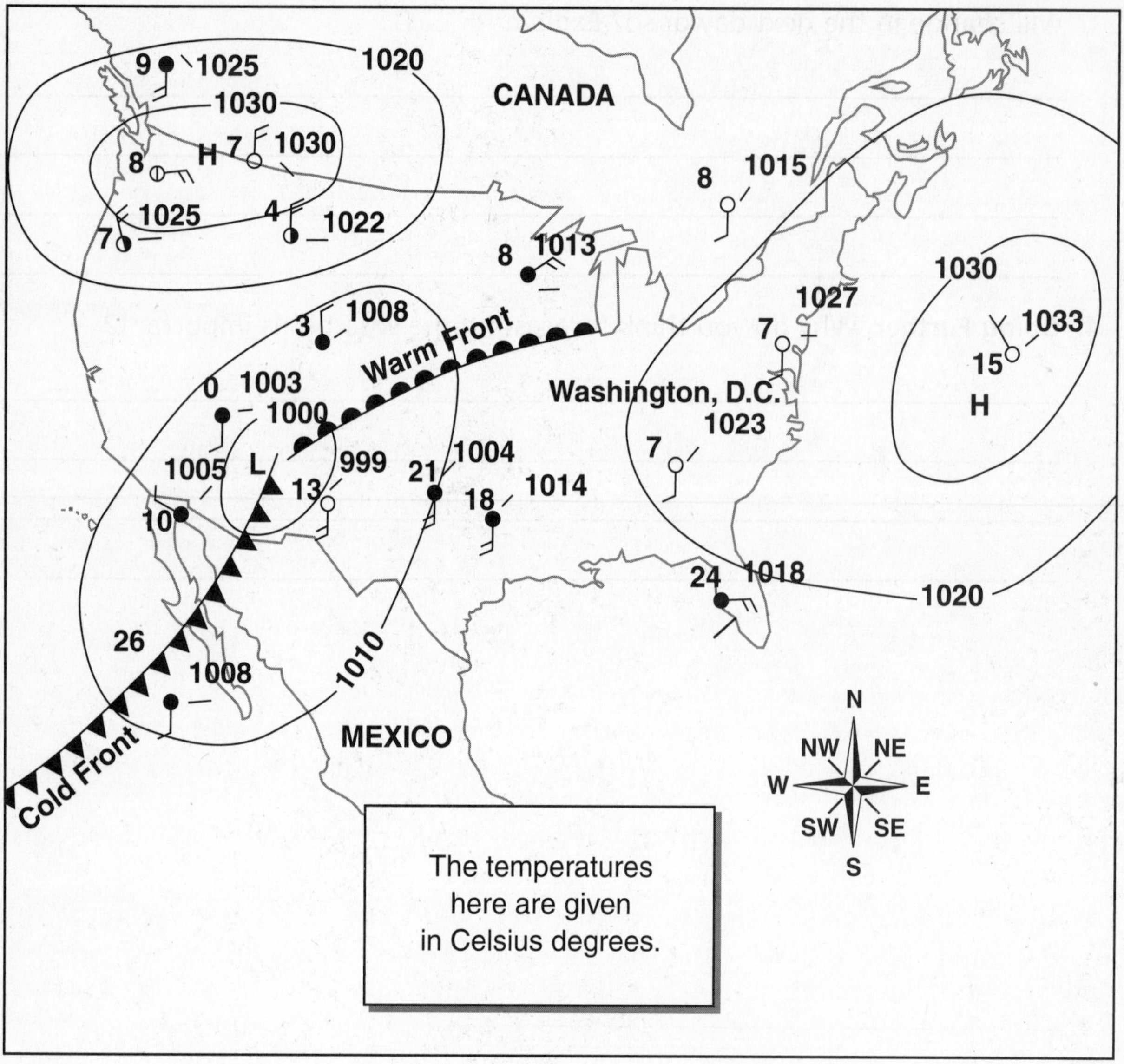
CANADA
MEXICO
Washington, D.C.
Warm Front
Cold Front
H
L
1020
1030
1025
1022
1015
1013
1008
1003
1000
1005
999
1004
1014
1027
1023
1033
1018
1010
N
NE
E
SE
S
SW
W
NW
The temperatures here are given in Celsius degrees.

Name ______________________ Date __________

Explore Activity
Lesson 6

# Where Do Tornadoes Occur?

**Hypothesize** Tornadoes strike all parts of the United States. However, they are more frequent in some regions than in others. Where in the U.S. is "tornado country"? How might you test your hypothesis? Write a **Hypothesis:**

Possible hypothesis: Students might hypothesize that the center of the country is "tornado country."

## Materials

- blue marker
- red marker
- map of U.S., including Alaska and Hawaii, on page 149

| State | Total | Average per Year | State | Total | Average per Year | State | Total | Average per Year | State | Total | Average per Year | State | Total | Average per Year |
|---|---|---|---|---|---|---|---|---|---|---|---|---|---|---|
| AL | 668 | 22 | HI | 25 | 1 | MA | 89 | 3 | NM | 276 | 9 | SD | 864 | 29 |
| AK | 0 | 0 | ID | 80 | 3 | MI | 567 | 19 | NY | 169 | 6 | TN | 360 | 12 |
| AZ | 106 | 4 | IL | 798 | 27 | MN | 607 | 20 | NC | 435 | 15 | TX | 4,174 | 139 |
| AR | 596 | 20 | IN | 604 | 20 | MS | 775 | 26 | ND | 621 | 21 | UT | 58 | 2 |
| CA | 148 | 5 | IA | 1,079 | 36 | MO | 781 | 26 | OH | 463 | 15 | VT | 21 | 1 |
| CO | 781 | 26 | KS | 1,198 | 40 | MT | 175 | 6 | OK | 1,412 | 47 | VA | 188 | 6 |
| CT | 37 | 1 | KY | 296 | 10 | NE | 1,118 | 37 | OR | 34 | 1 | WA | 45 | 2 |
| DE | 31 | 1 | LA | 831 | 28 | NV | 41 | 1 | PA | 310 | 10 | WV | 69 | 2 |
| FL | 1,590 | 53 | ME | 50 | 2 | NH | 56 | 2 | RI | 7 | 0 | WI | 625 | 21 |
| GA | 615 | 21 | MD | 86 | 3 | NJ | 78 | 3 | SC | 307 | 10 | WY | 356 | 12 |

## Procedure

1. **Infer** The table shown here lists how many tornadoes occurred in each state over a 30-year period. It also shows about how many tornadoes occur in each state each year. Look at the data in the table for two minutes. Now write what part of the country you think gets the most tornadoes.

   Tornadoes occur most frequently through the midsection of the country, from the Gulf Coast through the Great Plains.

2. Use the red marker to record the number of tornadoes that occurred in each state over the 30-year period. Use the blue marker to record the average number of tornadoes that occurred in a year in each state.

   Students should record their markings on the map.

Name______________________________ Date____________

**Explore Activity**
**Lesson 6**

## Drawing Conclusions

1. **Use Numbers** Which states had fewer than 10 tornadoes a year? Which states had more than 20 tornadoes a year?

   Fewer than 10: AK, AZ, CA, CT, DE, HI, ID, ME, MD, MA, MT, NV, NH, NJ, NM, NY, OR, RI, UT, VT, VA, WA, WV. More than 20: AL, CO, FL, GA, IL, IA, KS, LA, MS, MO, NE, ND, OK, SD, TX, and WI.

2. **Interpret Data** Which six states had the most tornadoes during the 30-year period?

   FL, IA, KS, NE, OK, and TX

3. **Interpret Data** Which part of the country had the most tornadoes?

   the midsection of the country

4. **Going Further: Communicate** Many people refer to a certain part of the country as "Tornado Alley." Which part of the country do you think that is? Why do you think people call it that? What else might these states have in common? Describe how you would go about finding the answer to that question.

   Students might suggest that "Tornado Alley" runs, like an alley, through the middle of the United States, from the Gulf Coast to the Great Plains. They might suggest that these areas share certain weather conditions that contribute to the formation of tornadoes, and that they could use encyclopedias to investigate these conditions.

Name______________________________ Date____________

**Explore Activity**
Lesson 6

**Inquiry**

Think of your own questions that you might like to test. Do tornadoes in "Tornado Alley" occur most often during certain times of the year?

My Question Is:

Possible answer: During which seasons do most tornadoes in "Tornado Alley" occur?

How I Can Test It:

Possible answer: I can compare seasonal weather maps from the states in "Tornado Alley."

My Results Are:

Possible answer: Most "Tornado Alley" tornadoes occur in spring and summer.

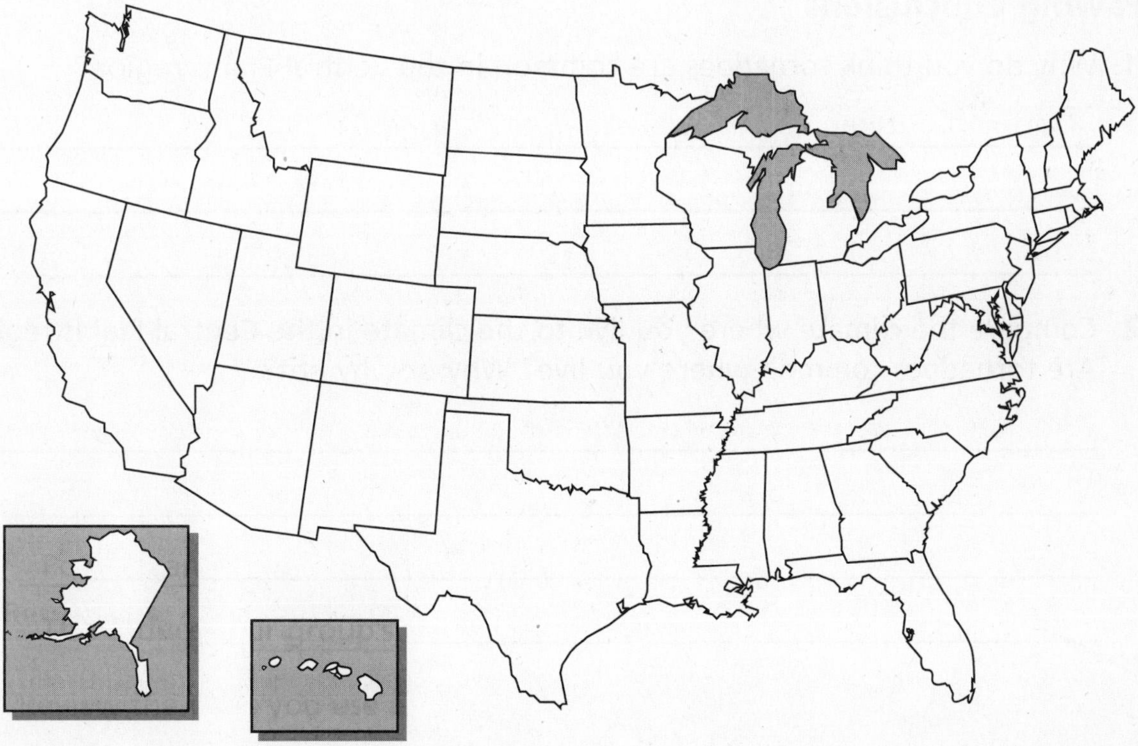

Name____________________ Date__________

Alternative Explore
Lesson 6

# In the Alley

## Procedure

**Materials**
- encyclopedias and other research materials

1. Find out about the weather conditions that cause tornadoes to form. Use encyclopedias and any other research materials that may be helpful. Write down what you learned.

   Tornadoes form where dry, cold air masses mix with warm, moist air masses.

2. Research the climate in the Central Plains region. What are conditions like there during the spring and early summer?

   During the spring and early summer, warm, moist air from the south or southwest meets cool, dry air from the west or northwest in the Central Plains region.

## Drawing Conclusions

1. Why do you think tornadoes are common in the Central Plains region?

   During the spring and early summer, the mixing of warm, moist air with cool, dry air in the Central Plains region causes tornadoes to form.

2. Compare the climate where you live to the climate in the Central Plains region. Are tornadoes common where you live? Why or why not?

   Answers will vary depending on the local climate.

Name ______________________ Date ____________

QUICK LAB

FOR SCHOOL OR HOME

Lesson 6

# Tornado in a Bottle

**Hypothesize** How does a tornado form?
Write a **Hypothesis:**

Possible hypothesis: Tornadoes are formed because when air begins to swirl, the pressure suddenly drops causing air to rush in, lowering pressure even further.

## Materials

- two 2-L plastic bottles
- duct tape
- water
- paper towel
- pencil

## Procedure

1. **Make a Model** Fill a 2-L plastic bottle one-third full of water. Dry the neck of the bottle, and tape over the top with duct tape. Use a pencil to poke a hole in the tape.
   Hole in tape should be small.
2. Place another 2-L plastic bottle upside down over the mouth of the first bottle. Tape the two bottles together.
3. **Observe** Hold the bottles by the necks so the one with the water is on top. Swirl them around while your partner gently squeezes on the empty bottle. Then place the bottles on a desk with the water bottle on top. Describe what you see.

   Students should describe that the water in the top bottle spins in a tornado-like motion as it flows into the bottom bottle.

Name ______________________ Date ____________

QUICK LAB
FOR SCHOOL OR HOME
Lesson 6

## Drawing Conclusions

4. **Infer** How is this like what happens when a tornado forms? Explain.

   The model is like a real tornado because the water, like a tornado, formed a funnel shape.

5. **Going Further** What kind of damage can tornadoes cause? Research newspaper articles and reference books to find out.

   My Hypothesis Is:

   Possible hypothesis: Tornadoes can cause great damage to people and property

   My Experiment Is:

   Research past occurrences of tornadoes in the United States. Record the kind of damage that the tornadoes caused in the areas they hit.

   My Results Are:

   Answers will vary. Students will record that tornadoes destroy houses and other buildings. They also hurt people, and sometimes can even kill people.

Name______________________________ Date____________

Explore Activity
Lesson 7

# What Do Weather Patterns Tell You?

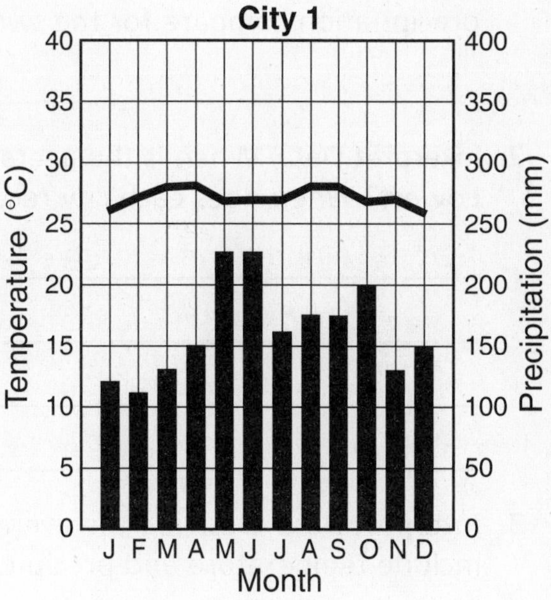


**Hypothesize** What factors are used to describe the average weather pattern of a region? How might you use graphs of year-round weather in different places to test your ideas? Write a **Hypothesis:**

Possible hypothesis: Patterns of seasonal temperature and precipitation, help define a region's weather pattern.

### Procedure

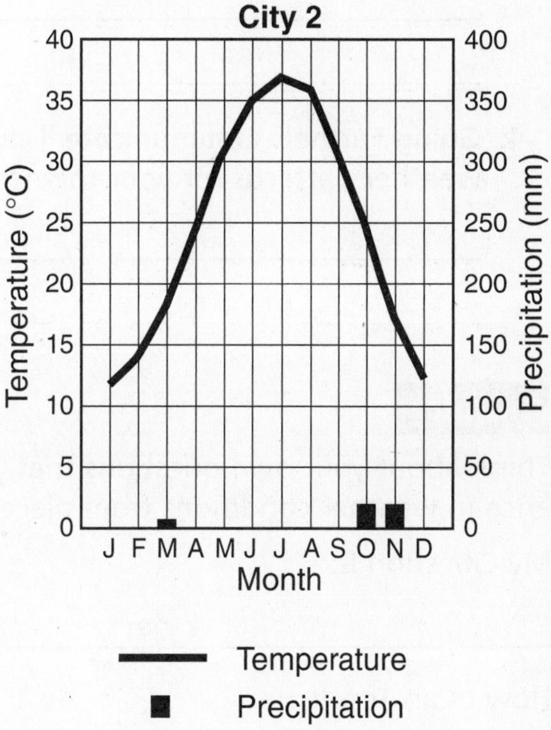


1. **Use Numbers** Look at the graph for city 1. The bottom is labeled with the months of the year. The left side is labeled with the temperature in degrees Celsius. Use this scale to read the temperature line. What is the average temperature in city 1 during July?

   The average July temperature for city 1 is 27°C.

2. **Use Numbers** The right side of the graph is labeled with millimeters of precipitation. Use this scale when reading the precipitation bars. What is the average precipitation in city 1 during July?

   The average July precipitation for city 1 is 160 mm.

3. Repeat steps 1 and 2 for city 2.

   average temperature is 37°C, and precipitation is 0 mm

Name ______________________ Date __________

Explore Activity
Lesson 7

## Drawing Conclusions

1. **Use Numbers** How do the annual amounts of precipitation compare for the two cities? Record your answer.

   City 1 has much higher annual precipitation than city 2.

2. **Interpret Data** When is the average temperature highest for each city? Lowest? When does each city receive the greatest amount of precipitation?

   City 1: highest temperature—March, April, August, September; lowest temperature—January and December. City 2: highest temperature—July; lowest temperature—January. City 1 gets its greatest precipitation in May and June; City 2 gets its in October and November.

3. **Interpret Data** Describe the average weather pattern for each city. Be sure to include temperature and precipitation, and their relationship to the seasons.

   City 1 has warm temperatures year–round, and receives a lot of rain each month. City 2 has a dry climate and temperatures change seasonally.

4. **Going Further: Communicate** How would you go about making a graph of the weather patterns for your town?

   Students might suggest recording daily temperatures and precipitation, calculating monthly averages and graphing data.

**Inquiry**

Think about your own questions that you might like to test. What causes the difference in weather conditions from place to place?

My Question Is:

Possible answer: What causes weather differences between cities?

How I Can Test It:

Possible answer: Choose two cities and compare locations, elevations, wind patterns, and other factors that affect weather.

My Results Are:

Answers will vary; students should identify factors affecting weather.

Name ______________________ Date ____________

Alternative Explore
Lesson 7

# Adapting to Climate Changes

## Procedure

1. Think about what might happen if you woke up one morning and found that the climate had drastically changed.
2. Write a story about it on a separate sheet of paper. Include how the climate changed and the adaptations you made in response to the climate changes.
Students should use humor as they describe the adaptations they would have to make.

## Drawing Conclusions

1. What adaptations did you make to the climate changes?
Answers will vary.
2. How was the climate different from before?
Answers will vary.
3. What are adaptations you make to regular climate changes during the year?
Answers will vary. Students might respond that during the summer they wear less clothing and drink more water; during the winter they wear more clothing and stay indoors.

Name ______________________ Date ____________

**Process Skill Builder**
Lesson 7

# Measure

## Modeling Climates

In this activity you will make a model of the soil conditions in two cities. Use the information in the graphs on page 153. The soil conditions you set up will model—or represent—the climates of the two cities. To do this, you will need to measure the amount of water you use and the amount of time you use the lamp.

### Materials

- stick-on notepaper
- marking pencil or pen
- 2 trays of dry soil
- spray bottle of water
- lamp
- thermometer

## Procedure

1. **Measure** Put 3 cm of dry soil into each tray. Label one tray City 1 and the other tray City 2.
2. **Use Numbers** What do the bars on each graph represent? List the amounts given by the bars for each month for each city.

The bars on the graphs represent the precipitation in each city.

| | Precipitation (mm) | | | Precipitation (mm) | |
|---|---|---|---|---|---|
| **Month** | **City 1** | **City 2** | **Month** | **City 1** | **City 2** |
| January | 120 | 0 | July | 160 | 0 |
| February | 110 | 0 | August | 170 | 0 |
| March | 130 | 10 | September | 170 | 0 |
| April | 150 | 0 | October | 200 | 25 |
| May | 230 | 0 | November | 130 | 25 |
| June | 230 | 0 | December | 150 | 0 |

Name ______________________ Date ____________

**Process Skill Builder**

Lesson 7

3. **Measure** Model the yearly precipitation and temperature like this: Let 5 minutes equal 1 month. One squeeze of water sprayed on the tray equals 10 millimeters of precipitation. Every minute the lamp is on equals 20 degrees of temperature. That means that from 0 to 5 minutes is January. During January the City 2 tray gets no water and the lamp shines on it for $\frac{3}{4}$ minute. The City 1 tray gets 12 squeezes of water and the lamp shines on it for $1\frac{1}{4}$ minutes.

4. **Make a Model** Model the two cities for all 12 months. Record your observations.

Students will probably note that the soil for City 2 remains considerably drier than that of City 1.

| Month | Observations: City 1 | Observations: City 2 |
|---|---|---|
| January | | |
| February | | |
| March | | |
| April | | |
| May | | |
| June | | |
| July | | |
| August | | |
| September | | |
| October | | |
| November | | |
| December | | |

## Drawing Conclusions

1. **Observe** Examine the soil in the trays. Compare them for the same months. How do they differ?

The model representing City 2 remains much drier than the model representing City 1.

2. **Communicate** How did measuring help you model climates?

Measuring the water and amount of time under the lamp made it possible to simulate two different sets of conditions in a way that allowed useful comparisons.

Name ______________________ Date __________

Explore Activity
Lesson 1

# Which Is More?

**Hypothesize** What properties do you use to compare the amounts of things? Are there different ways something can be "more" than other things? Write a **Hypothesis:**

Possible hypothesis: "More" can mean different things: an object may take up more space or have more mass.

**Materials**

- golf ball or wooden block
- blown-up balloon
- equal-pan balance
- ruler
- string
- box, such as a shoe box, big enough for the balloon to fit in
- pail of water

## Procedure: Design Your Own

1. **Observe** Look at the golf ball (or wooden block) and blown-up balloon. Which is "more"? Think of how one object could be "more":
   - more when you use a balance
   - more when you put it in water and see how much the water level goes up, and so on

   Record your observations.

   Students should observe that the balloon has more volume while the golf ball or block has more mass.

2. Use the equipment to verify one way that one object is more than another. Decide which of the two objects is "more" and which one is "less."

   Students' measurements should show that the balloon has more volume while the golf ball or block has more mass.

3. Repeat your measurements to verify your answer.

   Check students' measurements.

4. Now use different equipment to compare the two objects. Is the same object still "more"? Explain.

   Students' measurements should show that when a different property is measured, a different object has "more."

5. Repeat your measurements to verify your answer.

   Check students' measurements.

## Drawing Conclusions

1. **Communicate** Identify the equipment you used. Report your results.

   Equipment used and results will vary.

2. For each test, which object was more? In what way was it more than the other object?

   The report of the object that was more will depend on what measuring devise was used. Objects with a larger volume will be more if measured with the ruler or the bucket of water. Objects with more mass will be more if measured on the balance.

3. **Going Further: Experiment** What if you were given a large box of puffed oats and a small box of oatmeal? Which do you think would be more? Design an experiment to test your hypothesis. Tell what equipment you would use.

   Students might design an experiment to compare the two cereals using an equal-pan balance. They might also compare the amounts of cereal by pouring each separately into a common box.

### Inquiry

Think of your own questions that you might test. How might you compare two objects that are similar in size?

My Question Is:

Possible answer: How do a dictionary and box of tissue compare?

How I Can Test It:

Possible answer: I can use an equal-pan balance to compare the masses of the objects.

My Results Are:

Possible answer: These two objects are similar in volume but different in mass.

Name ______________________ Date __________

Alternative Explore
Lesson 1

# Which Bean Is More?

## Procedure

1. Count the number of jelly beans needed to fill one cup. Record the number in the table.
2. Repeat step 1 using dry beans.
3. Place each full cup on opposite sides of an equal-pan balance. Observe which cup has more mass and record your observation in the table.
4. Use a ruler to measure the length of a jelly bean. Record the length in the table.
5. Repeat step 4 using a dry bean.

## Materials

- small foam cups
- jelly beans
- dry beans
- equal-pan balance
- ruler

| | Jelly Beans | Dry Beans |
|---|---|---|
| Number to fill cup | | |
| Which has more mass? | | |
| Length | | |

## Drawing Conclusions

1. Which bean took more to fill the cup? Why?
   Results will vary. It takes more of the smaller beans to fill the cup since each takes up less space.
2. Which cup of beans had more mass? How could you tell?
   Results will vary. The balance tilts down on the side with the heavier cup.
3. Which bean was longer?
   Results will vary.

Name ______________________ Date __________

Process Skill Builder

Lesson 1

# Make a Model

## How Metal Boats Float

Think about objects that have more matter packed into the space they take up than water does. Will such objects sink or float in water? You have probably seen how a metal object like a nail or a spoon sinks in water. However, huge ships made of similar metal float even when they carry large cargoes. How is this possible? In this activity, you will make a model of a metal boat. Scientists use models to help them understand properties of matter. Working with a model makes experimenting easier. Experiment to see how boats are designed so that they can carry heavy cargo.

**Materials**

- household aluminum foil
- large paper clips
- pan of water

## Procedure

1. **Make a Model** Make a boat out of a 10-cm by 10-cm (4-in. by 4-in.) piece of aluminum foil. Then float it on water.
2. **Predict** Write down what you think will happen when you place more and more matter in the empty space of the boat. What steps should you follow to test your prediction? Be sure to use only the materials listed above.

   Students' predictions should indicate their understanding that flotation depends on both mass and volume.

3. **Experiment** Carry out your procedure, keeping a written record of what you observe.

   Possible answer: Students should observe that the boat sinks lower in the water as they add mass.

Name________________________________ Date____________

**Process Skill Builder**

Lesson 1

## Drawing Conclusions

1. **Communicate** How well did your results agree with your prediction?

   Most students will predict and verify that placing more matter in the boat causes the boat to sink.

2. Compare your model with those of your classmates. Which boat held the most clips? Why?

   Students' answers will vary depending on boat designs. Students should observe the relationship between the volume of the boat and the amount it can carry without sinking.

3. **Make a Model** The aluminum foil boat is a model of a steel ship. Use the way your boat floats to explain how a steel ship floats. Why was using a model of a large ship helpful?

   A steel ship will float if the ship and its cargo weigh less than an equal volume of water. A model is easier to experiment with than a full-sized ship.

4. **Communicate** What changed as more and more matter was added to the empty space of the boat? What happened as a result of this change?

   The density was increased, and the boat sank.


Use with textbook page E9

Name ______________________ Date __________

Explore Activity
Lesson 2

# How Do We Know What's "Inside" Matter?

**Materials**

- 3 identical, sealed, opaque boxes

**Hypothesize** How can you tell what is inside a sealed opaque box without opening it? What sorts of tests would you perform to try to identify its contents?

Write a **Hypothesis:**

Possible hypothesis: Differing masses or densities could be used to identify the contents.

## Procedure

1. **Observe** Examine the three boxes, but do not open them. You can lift them, shake them, listen to the noises they make, feel the way their contents shift as you move them, and so on. Record your observations.

   Students should note different sounds and feels as they shake the boxes. Some students may detect differences in mass.

2. **Infer** Try to determine what is in each box.

   Students might infer how many kinds of objects there are in a box. Some suggestions might further include that the objects are round or flat.

| Box | Observations | Object(s) |
|---|---|---|
| #1 | | |
| #2 | | |
| #3 | | |

## Drawing Conclusions

1. **Communicate** Describe what you think is in each box.

   Box #1 contains only paper clips; box #2 contains only marbles; Box #3 contains a mixture of paper clips and marbles.

2. How did you make your decision?

Possible answer: the decisions were based on feel and sound.

3. Do these boxes have anything in common? In what ways are they similar? In what ways are they different?

All boxes were cardboard, had identical sizes and shapes. But the objects inside each made different sounds when they were moved.

4. **Going Further: Experiment** What if you have a can of peanuts and a can of stewed tomatoes? The cans look the same except for the labels. Now what if your baby brother takes the labels off? You want the peanuts, but you don't want to open the tomatoes by mistake. What experiments can you do to find out what is inside—before you open the cans?

If the cans were shaken, the can of peanuts would make a rattling sound and the can of tomatoes would make a sloshing sound.

## Inquiry

Think of your own questions that you might test. How might I tell the difference between a liquid and a gas?

My Question Is:

Possible answer: Which container holds a liquid and which one holds a gas?

How I Can Test It:

Possible answer: Compare two bottles—one full of water and one containing air.

My Results Are:

Possible answer: I hear a sloshing sound when I shake the heavy bottle,but I hear nothing when I shake the bottle with air.

Name ________________________ Date ____________

Alternative Explore
Lesson 2

# What's in Me?

## Procedure

1. Form a group with several other students.
2. **Experiment** You must try to determine the contents of each of the boxes. Start by discussing what tests you will conduct to make observations that will help you infer the contents.
3. **Observe** Conduct your tests to determine the contents of each of the boxes. After each test, record your observations in the table.

**Materials**

- 2 sealed boxes of different sizes
- soft toy
- colored pencils or crayons

| | OBSERVATIONS | |
|---|---|---|
| Test | Smaller Box | Larger Box |
| 1 | Observations will vary. Tests might | include shaking the box to listen |
| 2 | to the noises made or holding it to | guess its weight. |

4. **Infer** Try to determine what is in each box.

## Drawing Conclusions

1. **Communicate** In the space provided, make a drawing of what you think is inside each box. Drawings will vary.

   Smaller Box                Larger Box

2. How did you make your decisions?

   Students should support their inferences with observations.

Name ______________________ Date ____________

QUICK LAB

FOR SCHOOL OR HOME

Lesson 2

# Modeling Molecules

**Hypothesize** How do different elements combine to form molecules? Write a **Hypothesis:**

Possible hypothesis: Pairs of elements combine to form molecules. Other students may suggest that any quantity of atoms or elements can be combined. Some students might suggest different shapes for the combinations that result.

## Materials

- large and small marshmallows
- toothpicks

## Procedure

1. Using small marshmallows for hydrogen atoms and large marshmallows for oxygen atoms, make two $H_2$ molecules and one $O_2$ molecule. Join the atoms with toothpicks.
2. **Use Numbers** Count the number of atoms of each type you have in your molecules. Record these numbers. Take this many more marshmallows and make as many water molecules as you can, using toothpicks to join the atoms.

   There are 4 hydrogen atoms and 2 oxygen atoms. To make water molecules, join 2 hydrogen atoms with every one oxygen atom.

## Drawing Conclusions

3. **Observe** How many water molecules did you make?

   Two water molecules.

4. **Infer** Why would real water molecules have properties different from real hydrogen and oxygen molecules?

   The properties of compounds are different than the properties of the elements that are in them.

Name ______________________ Date ____________

QUICK LAB

FOR SCHOOL OR HOME

Lesson 2

**5. Going Further** Describe other examples of elements combining to form new compounds. Write and conduct an experiment.

My Hypothesis Is:

Possible hypothesis: Carbon and oxygen atoms can combine to form carbon dioxide.

My Experiment Is:

Possible experiment: Repeat the above experiment using large marshmallows to represent carbon atoms and small marshmallows to represent oxygen atoms.

My Results Are:

Two oxygen atoms can combine with one carbon atom to form carbon dioxide ($CO_2$)

Name________________________ Date____________

Explore Activity
Lesson 3

# What Happens When Ice Melts?

**Hypothesize** How does the temperature change as a block of ice melts? Does it increase?

Write a **Hypothesis:**

Possible hypothesis: The temperature of the ice remains the same as the ice melts, and then increases after all the ice is melted.

## Materials

- ice cubes
- water
- graduated cylinder
- plastic or paper cup
- thermometer
- heat source (lamp or sunlight)
- watch or clock

## Procedure

1. **Measure** Put ice cubes in the cup. Add 50 mL of water to the cup. Swirl the ice-and-water mixture together for 15 seconds.
2. **Measure** Place the thermometer in the cup. Wait 15 seconds. Then read the temperature. Record your observation.

   Students should note a temperature of 0°C or 32° F.
3. **Measure** Put the cup under a heat source (lamp or sunlight). Take temperature readings every 3 minutes as the ice melts.

   As the ice melts, the temperature of the water remains constant.
4. **Measure** After all the ice has melted, continue taking temperature readings every 3 minutes for another 15 minutes.

   After the ice melts, the temperature of the water will rise.

| Time | Temperature (As Ice Melts) | Temperature (After Ice Melts) |
|---|---|---|
| 3 minutes | | |
| 6 minutes | | |
| 9 minutes | | |
| 12 minutes | | |
| 15 minutes | | |

Name ______________________ Date __________

**Explore Activity**
Lesson 3

## Drawing Conclusions

1. **Observe** What happened to the temperature as the ice melted?

The temperature remained constant.

2. **Hypothesize** Why do you think you got the results described in question 1?

The heat is being used to melt the ice, not raise the temperature of the water.

3. **Going Further: Predict** What do you think would happen if you didn't add any water to the ice? What do you think would happen if you added more water to the ice? Design an experiment to test each of your predictions. What do you think happens as you freeze water? How would you design an experiment to test your prediction?

The ice would melt more slowly if you didn't add any water to the ice. More water would allow the ice to melt more quickly. Once the water reaches the freezing point, the temperature remains the same until it is all frozen, then it starts to decrease again.

**Inquiry**

Think of your own questions that you might test. How might the intensity of heat affect melting ice?

My Question Is:

Possible answer: How would hotter temperatures affect the amount of time it takes ice to melt?

How I Can Test It:

Possible answer: Use two lamps to increase the heat or set the ice in the sunlight in the morning and again at noon.

My Results Are:

Possible answer: The ice melts faster in hotter temperatures.


Use with textbook page E35

Name ______________________ Date ____________



# Melting Temperature

## Procedure

**BE CAREFUL!** Do not touch the heated surface of the hot plate.

1. Form a group with several other students.
2. Select three samples from the set of melting samples.
3. Place the items on the aluminum foil or pie plate. Then place them on the hot plate.
4. **Observe** Note the order in which the items melt.

   Order will vary depending on items selected.

## Materials

- oven mitt
- goggles
- hot plate
- aluminum foil or pie plate
- melting samples (ice, wax, butter, chocolate, and mozzarella cheese)

## Drawing Conclusions

1. **Interpret Data** Organize the data by placing the item that melted last at the top of the list and the item that melted first at the bottom.

   **Order of Melting**

   Order will vary depending on items selected.

2. **Hypothesize** Why do you think you got the results described in your list?

   Possible answer: The item that melted first melts at a lower temperature than the other items.

Name ______________________ Date ____________

QUICK LAB

FOR SCHOOL OR HOME

Lesson 3

# Collapsing Bottles

**Hypothesize** How does heat affect an empty plastic bottle? How does cold affect it? Write a **Hypothesis:**

Possible hypothesis: Heat might make the bottle expand and cold might make the bottle contract.

## Materials

- flexible plastic bottle with screw cap
- pails of hot and ice-cold water

## Procedure

1. **Predict** How does heat affect an empty plastic bottle? What do you think will happen to a bottle when it is warmed? What do you think will happen to it when it is cooled? Record your predictions.

   The plastic bottle will expand when warmed and contract when cooled.

2. With the cap off, hold a bottle for a minute or two in a pail of hot tap water. Then screw the cap on tightly while the bottle is still sitting in the hot water.
3. **Experiment** Now hold the bottle in a pail of ice water for a few minutes.

## Drawing Conclusions

4. **Communicate** Record your observations.

   The bottle held in the warm water expanded. When placed in the ice water, the bottle contracted.

5. **Infer** Write out an explanation of why the bottle changed as it did. Be sure to use the idea of how molecules move at different temperatures.

   The air inside the bottle expanded when heated because the molecules moved faster and took up more space. When the bottle was cooled, the air inside contracted because the molecules moved slower and required less space.

Name________________________________ Date____________

QUICK LAB
FOR SCHOOL OR HOME
Lesson 3

**6. Going Further** Do gases also contract and expand with changing temperatures? Write and conduct an experiment.

My Hypothesis Is:

Possible hypothesis: Gases contract when cooled and expand when heated.

My Experiment Is:

Possible experiment: Inflate two balloons with air. Make sure each balloon is about the same size when inflated. Hold one balloon in a pail of hot water for a minute or two. Hold the other balloon in a pail of ice water for a few minutes. Describe what happens.

My Results Are:

Possible answer: The balloon held in the hot water will begin to expand and possibly pop. The hot water heats the balloon, making the air molecules move faster and faster, taking up more space. The balloon held in the cold, ice water will contract and shrink in size. The cold temperature slows the air molecules down, requiring less space.



Use with textbook page E41

Name ______________________ Date ____________

Explore Activity
Lesson 4

# How Can You Take Apart Things that Are Mixed Together?

**Materials**

- sample of substances mixed together
- hand lens
- toothpicks
- magnet
- paper (coffee) filters
- 2 cups or beakers
- water
- goggles

**Hypothesize** How can you separate substances that are mixed together in a way that they keep their properties?

Write a **Hypothesis:**

Possible hypothesis: Mixtures can be separated by the individual properties of their components, such as size, density, and solubility.

**Procedure: Design Your Own**

**BE CAREFUL!** Wear goggles. Do not taste your sample.

1. **Observe** Examine the sample your teacher gives you. It is made of different substances. One of the substances is table salt. What else does it seem to be made of? Record your observations.

   Encourage students to use visual clues such as size and color of the particles to help determine what the mixture might be made of.

2. **Experiment** Design and carry out an experiment to separate the various ingredients in your sample.

   Experiments should involve using several different properties.

| Sample | Observations |
|---|---|
| Color | |
| Size | |
| | |
| | |

Name____________________ Date__________

Explore Activity
Lesson 4

## Drawing Conclusions

1. **Infer** How many parts or substances were mixed into your sample? How did you reach that conclusion?

Four components could be separated from the mixture.

2. You knew one substance was salt. What properties of salt might help you separate it from the rest? Could you separate salt first? Why or why not?

Pouring water onto the substances will dissolve the salt. When the water evaporates, the salt will be left behind. Other substances can be filtered from the salt water to remove the salt.

3. How did you separate out the substances? How did you use the properties of these substances to separate them?

Possible answer: Iron was separated with a magnet. Foam pellets will float and can be skimmed off when water is added. Salt dissolves in water, but sand does not. Sand sinks, so the salt water can be poured off.

4. **Going Further: Experiment** What if you were given white sand and sugar mixed together? How would you separate the two ingredients?

Adding water to the mixture will dissolve the sugar, but not the sand. Filter the mixture to separate the sand from the sugar water solution.

**Inquiry**

Think of your own questions that you might test. Would magnetism help you separate iron filings from solids?

My Question Is:

Possible question: Would magnetism help you separate iron filings from sugar?

How I Can Test It:

Possible test: Use a magnet to separate iron filings from sugar.

My Results Are:

Possible answer: Magnetism can separate iron filings from sugar.

Name ____________________ Date __________

Alternative Explore

Lesson 4

# Separate by Dissolving

**Materials**

- salt
- ground wax
- goggles
- water
- coffee filter
- 2 plastic glasses
- spoon

**Procedure** BE CAREFUL! Wear goggles.

1. Prepare a mixture by placing a spoonful each of salt and ground wax into a plastic glass. Stir the mixture.
2. Add a little water to the glass.
3. Stir the contents until the salt dissolves. (Add more water if you need to.)
4. Tuck a coffee filter into a second plastic glass.
5. **Observe** Pour the mixture into the filter. Record your observations.

   The liquid passes through the filter and the wax is trapped in the filter.

6. Remove the filter. Place the glass of liquid in a sunny spot.
7. **Observe** After several days, observe the contents of the glass and record your observations.

   The water has evaporated and salt crystals have formed.

## Drawing Conclusions

1. At what point did you separate the wax from the salt? Explain your answer.

   When I poured the liquid through the filter, the salt (dissolved in water) passed through and the wax remained on the filter.

2. **Identify** What property did you use to separate the mixture? Explain your answer.

   Accept any reasonable explanation: Solubility; salt dissolves in water but wax doesn't.

Name ______________________ Date __________

QUICK LAB
FOR SCHOOL OR HOME
Lesson 4

# Solubility

**Hypothesize** Is a substance more soluble in one piece or in many pieces? Test your ideas. Write a **Hypothesis:**

Possible hypothesis: A substance broken into many pieces will dissolve faster.

## Materials

- water
- 3 cups
- 100 mL beaker
- sugar cubes

## Procedure

1. **Measure** Add 100 mL of water to each of 3 cups. Place a sugar cube in one of the cups, and stir until the cube is dissolved. Record the time it took to dissolve.

   Times will vary.

2. **Predict** Carefully break a second sugar cube into two pieces. How long do you think it will take to dissolve? Place the two pieces in a second cup of water, and stir until they dissolve. Record the time they took to dissolve.

   Predictions will vary. The time should be shorter than for step 1.

3. **Use Variables** Fold a piece of paper around a sugar cube, and carefully break the cube into many pieces. Pour the pieces into the third cup of water, and stir until dissolved. Record the dissolving time.

   The time should be the shortest yet.


Use with textbook page E58

Name ______________________ Date __________

QUICK LAB

FOR SCHOOL OR HOME

Lesson 4

## Drawing Conclusions

**4. Interpret Data** Construct a graph that illustrates your findings. Which sugar cube dissolved the fastest?

The sugar cube that was broken into the smallest pieces dissolved the fastest.

**5.** What conclusion can you make regarding dissolving time based on the experiment?

The time it takes for a substance to dissolve depends on what size the pieces of the substance are.

**6. Going Further** Think of your own question that you might like to test. Do different substances dissolve at the same rates?

My Hypothesis Is:

Possible hypothesis: Similar substances dissolve at different rates.

My Experiment Is:

Possible experiment: Substitute an equal amount of another substance such as salt for the sugar and repeat the experiment. Record your observations and compare them with your observations about the sugar dissolving.

My Results Are:

Possible answer: Answers will vary but students should observe that different substances dissolve at different rates.

Name ______________________ Date ____________

QUICK LAB

FOR SCHOOL OR HOME

Lesson 4

# Kitchen Colloids

**Hypothesize** What happens to cream when you whip it?

Write a **Hypothesis:**

Possible hypothesis: Whipping will change the consistency and volume of the cream.

## Materials

- whipping cream
- 2 bowls
- wire whisk
- ice

## Procedure

1. Pour some whipping cream into a bowl. Set this bowl in a bed of ice in another bowl. Let the cream and bowl chill.
2. **Experiment** Use a whisk to whip the cream until it becomes a fluffy texture.
3. **Observe** Let the cream warm and continue beating it. Observe how it changes. Record your observations.

   Beating the warm cream should reduce the volume. Continued agitation will turn the cream to butter.

## Drawing Conclusions

4. **Define** What kind of colloid is the whipped cream in step 2?

   Whipped cream is a foam. A foam is a gas spread through a liquid.

5. **Interpret Data** What is it made of?

   The gas in whipped cream is air. The liquid in whipped cream is water and fat.

6. **Infer** In step 3 you made a colloid. What is this colloid commonly known as? What do you think it is made of?

   The colloid is butter. Butter is primarily butterfat.


Use with textbook page E61

Name ______________________ Date ____________



7. **Going Further** What other colloids can you find in the kitchen? What are they made of? Write and conduct an experiment.

My Hypothesis Is:

Possible hypothesis: Gelatin dessert is a gel colloid.

My Experiment Is:

Possible experiment: Research what makes up gelatin dessert and which properties it has by using reference books.

My Results Are:

Possible answer: Gelatin dessert is a gel. A gel is a solid spread through a liquid. The solid in the gelatin is protein, and the liquid is water.

Name ______________________ Date __________

Explore Activity
Lesson 5

# How Can You Recognize a Change?

**Hypothesize** How can you tell if a substance changes into something else? What signs would you look for?

Write a **Hypothesis:**

Possible hypothesis: Gas bubbles are a sign of a substance changing into something else.

## Materials

- baking soda
- baking powder
- cornstarch
- salt
- iodine solution
- vinegar
- water
- wax paper
- permanent marker
- 4 toothpicks
- 3 droppers
- 4 plastic spoons
- 7 small cups
- goggles

**Procedure** BE CAREFUL! Wear goggles.

1. Copy the grid on page 182 on wax paper with a marking pen. Using a spoon, put a pea-sized amount of cornstarch in each of the three boxes in the first row.
2. **Observe** Use a dropper to add five drops of water to the cornstarch in the first column. Stir with a toothpick. Record your observations.

   Students should notice no change in the cornstarch.

3. **Experiment** Using a different dropper, add five drops of vinegar to the cornstarch in the second column. Stir with a new toothpick. Record your observations.

   Students should notice no change in the cornstarch.

4. **Observe** Use a third dropper to add five drops of iodine solution to the cornstarch in the third column. Record your observations. CAUTION: Iodine can stain and is poisonous.

   Students should notice that the cornstarch turns blue/black in iodine.

5. **Experiment** Repeat steps 1–4 for baking powder, baking soda, and salt.

Baking powder produces a few bubbles when mixed with water and iodine; it produces many more bubbles with vinegar, and turns blue/black with iodine solution. Baking soda bubbles vigorously with vinegar, and produces no reaction with the other liquids. Salt may dissolve in the liquids.

## Drawing Conclusions

1. **Infer** In which boxes of the grid do you think substances changed into new substances? Explain your answers.

New substances were formed with cornstarch and iodine solution; baking powder and water, vinegar, and iodine solution; and baking soda and vinegar. With salt no new substances were formed.

2. **Going Further: Infer** Your teacher will give you samples of two unknown powders. Use what you have learned to identify these powders. Report on your findings.

The unknowns can be identified using the above information.
No reaction: salt;
Only fizzles with vinegar: baking soda;
Turns blue/black with no other reaction: cornstarch;
Reacts with all: baking powder.

Name ______________________ Date ____________

Explore Activity
Lesson 5

**Inquiry**

Think of your own questions that you might test. What evidence might show a liquid changing to a gas?

My Question Is:

Possible answer: What would I look for when changing water from a liquid form to a gaseous form?

How I Can Test It:

Possible answer: I can boil water to change states.

My Results Are:

Possible answer: Steam shows me that water is changing states.

| | Water | Vinegar | Iodine solution |
|---|---|---|---|
| Cornstarch | | | |
| Baking powder | | | |
| Baking soda | | | |
| Salt | | | |

Name________________________ Date____________



# Form Rust

## Procedure

1. Wet the inside of the test tube by filling it with water. Then pour out the water.
2. Place a small amount of steel wool in the bottom of the test tube.
3. Fill the beaker with water.
4. Place your finger over the opening of the test tube. Turn the test tube upside down. Continuing to block the opening with your finger, place the test tube in the beaker of water.
5. Let go of the test tube and place the beaker where it will not be disturbed.
6. **Observe** Examine the test tube over the next few days. Record your observations.

The steel wool rusts, forming a brownish red substance.

## Materials

- steel wool (iron)
- water
- test tube
- beaker

## Drawing Conclusions

1. **Infer** What evidence did you observe that a chemical change took place?

Possible answer: Some of the steel wool changed color.

2. What substances do you think reacted to produce the chemical change?

steel (iron) and gas in the air (oxygen)

Name ______________________ Date __________

**Process Skill Builder**
Lesson 5

# Experiment

## Preventing Rust

You've learned that steel forms rust when exposed to oxygen and moisture. Rusting can ruin metal objects. Can you find a way to stop or slow rusting? In this activity you will experiment to try to find the answer. In order to experiment, you need to do the following things. Form a hypothesis. Design a control. Carry out your experiment. Analyze and communicate your results.

**Materials**

- steel nails and sandpaper
- paper cups
- dilute salt water
- goggles

**Procedure** BE CAREFUL! Wear goggles.

1. **Hypothesize** You can make a steel nail rust by placing it in water. Think of a way to protect a steel nail from rusting under such conditions. Write an explanation of why you think your method will work.

   Students might suggest that since the nail rusts in water, using a different liquid or coating the nail might protect it from rusting.

2. **Experiment** To test your method of rust protection, you need a control nail kept under normal conditions. Each experimental nail will have just one condition (variable) change. For example, what if you wanted to make a nail rust? You might leave one nail in a clean, empty jar (the control). You might put another in water. You might put a third in lemon juice. The amount of rusting that occurs is called the *dependent variable*. Write out how you will set up the experimental and control the nails for your experiment.

   Students should test nails under different conditions, including a dry nail (the control) and a nail in a different liquid. Make sure students change only one condition for each nail.

3. **Experiment** Carry out your experiment, and record your observations. Draw how the nails looked at the end of your experiment.

Students should observe which methods protect nails from rusting and which do not.

## Drawing Conclusions

1. **Infer** Write out a description of how well your hypothesis agreed with your results. Be sure to compare the experimental nail with the control nail.

Students' hypotheses might or might not agree with their results. If the results do not agree, students should explain why.

2. **Communicate** Why did you need a control in this experiment?

A control remains unchanged during an experiment. It provides a way to make comparisons so that you can tell if a variable is responsible for a given result.

Name_________________________ Date___________

Explore Activity
Lesson 6

# Which Are Acids and Which Are Bases?

**Materials**

- red and blue litmus paper
- wide-range pH paper
- plastic cups
- labels
- goggles
- gloves
- apron
- household solutions

**Hypothesize** Can you test whether or not a solution is an acid or a base? Test your ideas. Write a **Hypothesis:**

Possible hypothesis: You can test many substances

to see if they are acids or bases.

**Procedure** BE CAREFUL! Wear goggles, gloves, and an apron.

1. **Predict** Which solutions do you think are acids and which are bases? Write your predictions in a chart like the one shown below.
2. **Observe** Vinegar is an acid. Put a small amount in a cup, and mark the cup with a label. Test by dippng a piece of red litmus paper into the vinegar. Record the result in your table. Repeat with a piece of blue litmus paper. Litmus paper is a material that allows you to tell which solutions are acids and which are bases.
3. **Classify** Test all of your other solutions in the same way, and record your results.

| Sample | Predict: Acid or Base? | Effect on Red Litmus | Effect on Blue Litmus | Result: Acid or Base? |
|---|---|---|---|---|
| Vinegar | ACID | | | ACID |
| Baking soda | | | | |
| Lemon juice | | | | |

**Drawing Conclusions**

1. Which samples are acids? How do you know?

vinegar, orange juice, lemon juice, carbonated beverage, tea; samples

turned blue litmus paper red

2. Which samples are bases? How do you know?

antacid in water, baking soda in water, powdered detergent in water, dilute ammonia cleanser; samples turned red litmus paper blue

3. **Measure** Now test each sample with a small strip of pH paper. Match the color of the paper to the color scale on the holder, and find the pH.

Have students record the pH of each sample and then order them from lowest to highest in a chart.

4. **Going Further: Interpret Data** Look at your data. Do acids have higher or lower pH values than bases? Which sample is most acidic? Which is most basic? How do you know?

Acids have lower pH values. Depending on how dilute the samples are, vinegar will likely be the most acidic and detergent the most basic. Depth of color of litmus paper or the color of the pH paper will indicate pH. The sample with the lowest number is the most acidic; the highest number is the most basic.

## Inquiry

Think of your own question that you might like to test. Could you test whether a solution is an acid or a base if you only had red litmus paper?

My Question Is:

Possible answer: Could you test whether a solution is an acid or a base if you only had red litmus paper?

How I Can Test It:

Possible answer: Dip the litmus paper in the solution.

My Results Are:

Possible answer: If the litmus paper turns blue, the solution is a base. If the litmus paper stays red, the solution is either an acid or is neutral.

Name ______________________ Date ____________

Alternative Explore

Lesson 6

# Cleaning Pennies

**Materials**

- water and baking soda solution
- vinegar
- 2 paper cups for each group
- enough dirty pennies to provide 2 pennies per group of students

## Procedure

1. Work in a group. Place one penny in the cup of water and baking soda solution. Place one penny in the cup of vinegar.
2. Swish the pennies around in both cups.
3. Take the pennies out of the cups. Record the results.

   The pennies in the cup of vinegar are cleaner than those in the water and baking soda solution.

## Drawing Conclusions

1. Does vinegar or baking soda clean pennies better?

   vinegar

2. What other solutions might give similar results?

   Possible answers: Lemon juice, cola, ammonia, hydrogen peroxide, tea.

Name ____________________ Date __________

QUICK LAB
FOR SCHOOL OR HOME
Lesson 6

# Mystery Writing with a Base

**Hypothesize** Can grape juice be used to indicate the presence of a base substance? Test your ideas. Write a **Hypothesis:**

Possible hypothesis: Grape juice can be used to indicate the presence of a base.

## Materials

- baking soda
- grape juice
- cotton swabs
- white drawing paper

## Procedure

1. Using a cotton swab, write a short message to your partner on a piece of paper with a baking soda solution.
2. Put the paper aside, and allow it to completely dry. After it is dry, give it to your partner.
3. Can you read the message your partner gave you? You probably cannot. Use another cotton swab and gently "paint" the paper with grape juice.
4. **Observe** What happened when you painted the paper with the grape juice?

The baking soda solution changed color in the presence of grape juice and the "message" appeared.

Name ______________________ Date ____________

QUICK LAB
FOR SCHOOL OR HOME
Lesson 6

## Drawing Conclusions

**5. Infer** Is the grape juice an indicator? Why or why not?

Yes, the grape juice is an indicator because it changed color in the presence of a base.

**6. Going Further** Think of your own question that you might like to test. Would the grape juice work as an indicator if you used an acidic solution instead of a basic solution?

My Hypothesis Is:

Possible answer: The grape juice would work as an indicator if I used an acidic solution instead of a basic solution.

My Experiment Is:

Possible answer: Make a solution using an acid such as lemon juice and repeat the experiment.

My Results Are:

Possible answer: Answers will vary but students should observe that the grape juice's color change, if any, was not nearly as dramatic as with the basic solution. Therefore, the grape juice would not make the best indicator for an acidic solution.

Name ______________________ Date ____________

Explore Activity
Lesson 7

# How Well Do Batteries Provide Energy?

**Materials**

For each circuit to be tested:

- battery
- flashlight bulb
- 2 wires

**Hypothesize** Is it better to buy heavy-duty batteries or less expensive ones? Which last longer? Which ones are really the least expensive to use? Write a **Hypothesis:**

Possible hypothesis: The more expensive battery will last longer and cost less to use.

## Procedure

1. **Experiment** Connect one end of a wire to the light bulb. Connect the other end of the wire to the battery. Do the same for the other wire. Record what time the light bulb went on. Record the type, size, and brand of battery you used.

   Possible answers will vary.

2. **Observe** Examine the light bulb every 15 minutes to see if it is still lit. Record the time the light bulb goes off.

   AAA and AA batteries will wear out faster than C or D cells.

3. Repeat the experiment using another type or brand of battery.

   You might have each pair of students use a different type or brand of battery and combine the results.

| Time | Observations |
|---|---|
| 15 minutes | |
| 30 minutes | |
| 45 minutes | |
| 1 hour | |
| 1 hr. 15 min. | |
| 1 hr. 30 min. | |

Name ______________________ Date ____________

Explore Activity
Lesson 7

## Drawing Conclusions

1. **Use Numbers** Divide the time each battery lasted by the cost of that type of battery. Share your results with your classmates.

   Provide students with the cost of each type of battery used.

2. On another piece of paper, make a graph of the class's results. Which batteries lasted the longest? Which batteries cost the least per hour of use? Were some brands longer lasting? Were some brands cheaper to use than others?

   Graphs should compare size of battery, type of battery, brand of battery, length of service, cost of service, and chemicals.

3. **Infer** Are the cheapest batteries the best buy? Are the longest lasting batteries the best buy?

   Answers will depend on the analysis of the data. In general, larger cells will last longer because they contain more chemicals to produce the current and probably cost less per hour to use.

4. **Going Further: Interpret Data** When might you choose the longest lasting batteries? The least expensive batteries? The batteries that cost the least per hour of use? Explain.

   Possible answer: You might choose the longest lasting batteries when you don't want to run out of electricity, such as for a bicycle light, portable TV, or portable radio.

**Inquiry**

Think of your own questions that you might test. What other factors affect the cost effectiveness of batteries?

My Question Is:

Possible answer: Do alkaline cells last longer than regular cells?

How I Can Test It:

Repeat the experiment with two different kinds of batteries, compare results.

My Results Are:

Possible answer: Alkaline cells last longer than regular cells.

Name ______________________ Date __________

Alternative Explore
Lesson 7

# Flashlight Test

### Materials

- flashlight with new batteries

### Procedure

1. Turn on the flashlight. Place the flashlight so you can easily observe its light.
2. **Observe** Record the time and whether the flashlight is lit in the table.
3. **Observe** Every 15 minutes throughout the day, repeat step 2 until the flashlight goes out. (If needed, continue the table on separate piece of paper.)

| Time | Is flashlight still lit? |
|---|---|
| | |
| | |
| | |
| | |
| | |

### Drawing Conclusions

1. How long did the flashlight stay lit?

   Answers will vary.

2. **Compare and Contrast** Find the cost of the flashlight batteries from your teacher, then calculate the cost per hour of using the flashlight. Show your calculations. Compare your results with those of others.

   Answers will vary.

Name ______________________ Date ____________

QUICK LAB

FOR SCHOOL OR HOME

Lesson 7

# Measure Electricity

**Hypothesize** Can electricity affect a magnet? Can a magnet be used to measure electricity? Write a **Hypothesis:**

Possible hypothesis: Electricity can cause a magnet to move, so a magnet could be used to detect an electric current.

## Materials

- compass
- 5 m of fine varnish-coated wire
- sandpaper
- 1.5-V battery and bulb circuit

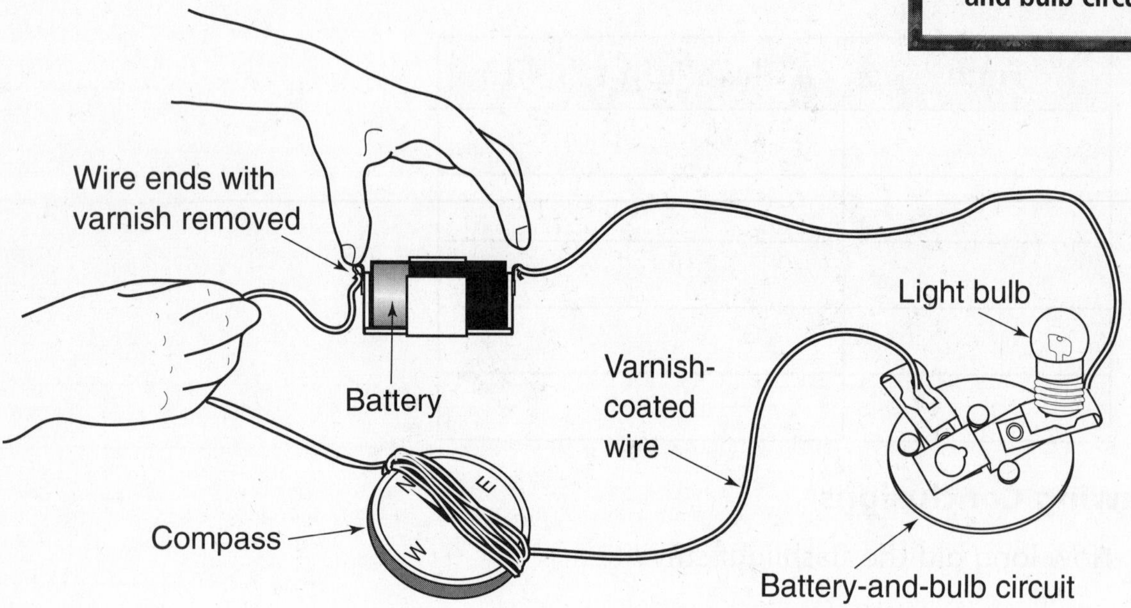


## Procedure

1. Wrap fine varnished wire around a compass. Use sandpaper to remove the coating from the ends of the wire.
2. Turn the compass until the needle is lined up with the coils of wire.
3. Keeping the compass this way, connect the ends of the wire to a circuit of a battery and small light bulb. See the diagram.
4. **Observe** What happens to the compass needle as you connect and disconnect the circuit? Record your observations.

   Students should note that the compass needle moves.

Name ______________________ Date ____________

QUICK LAB

FOR SCHOOL OR HOME

Lesson 7

## Drawing Conclusions

5. How did you know when electricity was flowing in the circuit?

A lit light bulb indicates that current is flowing in a circuit.

6. **Observe** When electricity was flowing, what did the compass needle do?

The current caused the compass needle to move or change direction.

7. **Infer** How do you think the needle would move if you used a less powerful battery?

Students might suggest that the needle would move less or it would move slower.

8. **Going Further** How do some animals use electric fields? Write and conduct an experiment.

My Hypothesis Is:

Possible hypothesis: Electric eels use electric fields to survive.

My Experiment Is:

Possible experiment: Conduct research on electric eels using reference books and magazines.

My Results Are:

Possible answer: Electic eels use a weak, low-voltage electric field to detect their food, and then they release an electric charge to kill or stun their prey.

Name ______________________ Date ____________

Explore Activity

Lesson 1

# How Fast Does a Spring Move Objects?

**Materials**

- 3 masses (washers or AAA batteries)
- metal ruler 30.5 cm (12 in)
- rubber bands
- clock with second hand
- graph paper
- goggles

**Hypothesize** Will changing the amount of mass affect the swinging of a hanging mass? Test your ideas.

Write a **Hypothesis:**

Possible hypothesis: More mass will swing slowly and less far than a smaller mass.

**Procedure** BE CAREFUL! Wear goggles.

1. Attach a mass to the end of a metal ruler with a rubber band. Hold the ruler tightly against the edge of a table as shown so it can act like a spring.
2. **Use Numbers** Pull the mass back 5 cm (2 in.), and release it crisply. Count and record how many swings the mass completes in ten seconds.

   Answers will vary.

3. **Predict** How will adding more mass to the end of the ruler affect how fast it swings back and forth? Record your predictions.

   The mass is inversely proportional to the number of vibrations in a given period of time. If the mass is doubled, the number of vibrations in the given time period should be halved.

4. Add a second mass, and repeat the procedure. Repeat again with a third mass.

## Drawing Conclusions

1. **Infer** Why does the ruler move the attached mass when it is pulled back and released?

   The ruler acts like a spring, exerting a force to move itself back to its original position after being pulled back.

Name ________________________ Date ____________

**Explore Activity**
Lesson 1

2. **Observe** What effect did increasing the mass have on how fast the mass was swung back and forth by the ruler?

Increasing the mass decreased how fast the mass swung back and forth.

3. **Hypothesize** Why do you think the increase in mass had this effect?

A greater mass is harder to set in motion (accelerate) than a smaller mass.

4. **Interpret Data** Make a graph of your results. What two variables should you plot?

The variables should be the mass (or number of masses) on the x-axis and the number of swings in ten seconds on the y-axis.

5. **Going Further: Predict** Use your graph to estimate how many swings would be observed in ten seconds when four masses are attached to the ruler.

Answers should show that the mass is inversely proportional to the number of vibrations.

**Inquiry**

Think of your own question that you might like to test. How would the length of a ruler affect its swing?

My Question Is:

Possible question: How would the length of a ruler affect its swing?

How I Can Test It:

Possible test: Repeat the experiment with either a longer ruler or by attaching the ruler so that it is shorter.

My Results Are:

Possible answer: A longer ruler should take longer to swing, while a shorter ruler should take less time to swing.

Name________________________ Date____________

Alternative Explore

Lesson 1

# Measuring Mass

## Procedure

1. Attach a rubber band to an empty laboratory cart. Stretch the rubber band back as far as possible.
2. Now release the cart. Observe its speed.
3. Repeat the experiment, this time loading the cart with weights.
4. Compare and contrast the speed of the empty and the loaded carts.

## Materials

- laboratory carts
- weights
- rubber bands

## Drawing Conclusions

1. Which cart moved faster? Why?

   The empty cart moved faster than the loaded cart because it had less mass.

2. What might happen if you repeated the experiment, filling the first cart with rocks and the second with feathers? Explain the results.

   The cart with the rocks would move slower than the cart with the feathers. Rocks are denser than feathers, so a cart full of rocks would have more mass than the same cart full of feathers.

Name ______________________________ Date ____________

QUICK LAB

FOR SCHOOL OR HOME

Lesson 1

# Using a Position Grid

**Hypothesize** How can you show an object's position relative to other objects? Test your ideas. Write a **Hypothesis:**

Creating a map with a scale can show objects' relative positions.

**Materials**

- graph paper

## Procedure

1. Make a grid. A grid has rows and columns labeled with letters and numbers. Each box in the grid has a particular position. The position of any box is given by a number and a letter, such as box A5 or box F2. Make a grid that goes from 1 to 29 across and from A to G down. You may wish to use graph paper. Follow the directions below to find out with your grid why the snail didn't move!

| | 1 | 2 | 3 | 4 | 5 | 6 | 7 | 8 | 9 | 10 |
|---|---|---|---|---|---|---|---|---|---|---|
| A | | | | | | | | | | |
| B | | | | | | | | | | |
| C | | | | | | | | | | |
| D | | | | | | | | | | |
| E | | | | | | | | | | |
| F | | | | | | | | | | |
| G | | | | | | | | | | |

The position grid should spell out "inertia."

2. Find each box, and shade it in with a colored pencil.

E27, B8, F24, D15, B29, C20, D5, F14, D29, B3, D11, B16, F3, D7, B27, B2, B11, F27, B20, F12, B23, D8, E17, F20, F23, C6, E2, E24, B10, B1, F10, C29, C2, F17, D24, E8, B15, E14, F1, B12, F5, D16, B21, B24, D27, C5, C10, E29, E7, B5, C14, C24, C16, E20, D2, C27, D10, C8, D17, E28, E10, D6, F25, D20, D14, F8, F29, B19, B14, F11, E5, B25, F2, B28

Name ______________________ Date ____________

QUICK LAB

FOR SCHOOL OR HOME

Lesson 1

# Drawing Conclusions

**3.** Why did the snail not want to move?

The snail had inertia.

**4. Infer** How is the grid that spelled out the reason for the snail not moving like the streets shown on a map of a city? How are street addresses like the letters and numbers that labeled the grid?

Streets at right angles to each other are like the rows and columns of the grid. Street addresses show positions along streets, as the numbers and letters show positions along the grid.

**5. Going Further: Predict** How might the answer change if you reversed the numbers and went from 29 to 1 from left to right?

The word "inertia" would appear backwards like in a mirror.

Name ______________________ Date ____________

Explore Activity
Lesson 2

# How Does Force Affect an Object's Motion?

**Materials**

- toy car
- 2 boards with hooks for rubber bands
- rubber bands
- meterstick
- masking tape
- goggles

**Hypothesize** Will changing the force applied to an object affect its motion? Test your ideas.

Write a **Hypothesis:**

Possible hypothesis: Increasing the force will affect an object in motion.

**Procedure** BE CAREFUL! Wear goggles.

1. Place a 15-cm (6-inch) strip of masking tape on the floor for a starting line. Hold two boards on either side of the starting line with a rubber band stretched between them.
2. **Measure** Launch a toy car along the floor as shown. The car should be pulled back against the rubber band exactly 5 cm (2 inches) prior to its release. Measure how far the car travels.

   Answers will vary.

3. **Observe** Repeat step 2 twice more, and average the three distances.
4. **Predict** What will happen when you use one, then two more rubber bands to launch the toy car? Test your prediction. Record your findings.

   The car should travel a greater distance when using additional rubber bands to launch it. Answers will vary depending on students' predictions.

**Drawing Conclusions**

1. **Interpret Data** When did the car move farthest on average—when one, two or three rubber bands were used?

   Students should note that the car traveled farther and farther as more rubber bands were added. This is because more force is being applied to the car.

2. **Infer** How is the distance traveled by the car in any trial related to the speed it was given by the rubber band? Why?

The greater the speed, the longer it takes the force of friction to bring the toy car to a stop.

3. **Going Further: Predict** If you taped a second toy car on top of the first and launched them with two rubber bands, how far would the cars travel? Test your prediction. Record and explain your observations.

It should travel a shorter distance because the mass is greater.

## Inquiry

Think of your own question that you might like to test. What would happen if you changed the surface that the cars were rolling on?

My Question Is:

Possible question: What would happen if you changed the surface that the cars were rolling on?

How I Can Test It:

Possible test: Place a long rug on the floor and run the tests on it instead of the floor.

My Results Are:

Possible answer: The rug causes the cars to not travel as far.

Name ______________________ Date __________

Alternative Explore
Lesson 2

# Accelerating Masses

**Materials**
- balls of differing weights
- weighing scale
- measuring tape

## Procedure

1. Throw each of the various balls as far as you can. Note that if you throw the balls at a 45-degree angle with the ground, you can achieve the greatest distance.
2. Measure the distance that each ball traveled before it hit the ground.
3. Weigh each ball.
4. Fill in the table showing how much each ball weighed and how far it traveled.

| Ball | Weight | Distance traveled |
|---|---|---|
| #1 | | |
| #2 | | |
| #3 | | |
| #4 | | |

## Drawing Conclusions

Which ball traveled the greatest distance? Why?

The ball that weighed the least traveled the farthest because it had less mass.

Name ______________________ Date __________

QUICK LAB

FOR SCHOOL OR HOME

Lesson 2

# Racing Balloon Rockets

**Hypothesize** What forces work to make a balloon rocket go? Test your ideas. Write a **Hypothesis:**

Possible hypothesis: The air coming out the back of the rocket makes it go forward.

## Materials

- soda straw
- tape
- balloon
- string

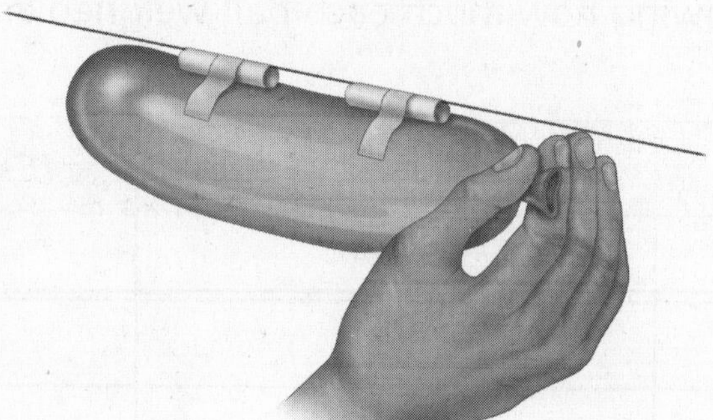

**Procedure**

1. Look at the picture of how to construct a balloon rocket. Thread several pieces of soda straw onto the string. Then stretch the string tightly between two chairs.
2. **Observe** Blow up a balloon. Hold the neck closed with your fingers while your partner tapes two of the straw pieces to the balloon. Let go of the balloon, and watch what it does! Record your observations.

   The balloon shoots away down the string.

3. **Observe** How does the direction in which the balloon moves compare with the direction in which the air is forced out?

   The balloon moved in the opposite direction from the air that escaped from the balloon.

4. **Infer** Is there an unbalanced force on the balloon? In which direction does it push?

Yes, an unbalanced force acts on the balloon in the direction the balloon is moving.

5. **Going Further** Think of your own questions that you might like to test. How would adding a second balloon affect your rocket's distance? Why?

My Question Is:

Possible question: How would adding a second balloon affect my rocket's distance?

How I Can Test It:

Possible test: Prepare a balloon rocket using two balloons. Compare the distances that it traveled with the distances your one-balloon rocket traveled. Record your observations.

My Results Are:

Possible answer: The two-balloon rocket traveled approximately twice as far as the one-balloon rocket. This is because the force was doubled.

Name_______________________ Date___________

Explore Activity
Lesson 3

# Does Weight Affect How Fast an Object Falls?

**Hypothesize** Do objects of different weights fall at the same speed? Test your ideas.

Write a **Hypothesis:**

Possible hypothesis: Two objects of different masses when dropped at the same time, will fall at the same rate.

## Materials

- table tennis ball
- golf ball
- pencil
- eraser
- goggles

## Procedure

1. **Predict** Do heavy objects fall faster than lighter objects? Record your prediction and your reasons for making it.

   A heavy and light object fall at the same rate. A 2-kg object is pulled on by twice the force of a 1-kg object, but its mass is also twice as great, so it has the same acceleration as the 1-kg object.

2. **Observe** Stretch out your arms in front of you at shoulder height. Hold two different balls—one in each hand—at the same height and drop them at exactly the same time. Listen for them to hit the floor. Which one hit the floor first? Record your results.

   Balls should hit the ground at the same time.

3. **Experiment** Repeat step 2 several more times to be sure your observations are accurate. Try dropping a pencil or an eraser at the same time as one of the balls. Record your observations.

   Objects should hit the ground at the same time unless one has more air resistance.

Name ______________________ Date ____________

**Explore Activity**
Lesson 3

## Drawing Conclusions

1. **Observe** Which ball hit the ground first?

   Both balls hit the ground at the same time.

2. **Observe** When you dropped different objects, which hit first, the heavier or the lighter?

   They still hit the ground at the same time.

3. **Hypothesize** Suggest an explanation for what you observed.

   Students may form different hypotheses, but one possible answer is that the force of gravity on the heavier ball is greater because its mass is greater, but the acceleration for the two balls is the same.

4. **Going Further: Experiment** Take two pieces of paper. Wad one into a tight ball. Leave the other alone. When you drop the two pieces of paper as you did the golf ball and table tennis ball, which will hit the ground first? Test your prediction. Explain your results.

   The piece of paper formed into a tight ball will hit the ground first because it encounters less air resistance.

**Inquiry**

Think of your own question that you might like to test. Would the results change if you dropped a very light object, such as a paperclip, with one of the balls?

My Question Is:

Possible question: Would the results change if you dropped a very light object, such as a paperclip, with one of the balls?

How I Can Test It:

Possible test: Substitute a paper clip for one of the balls and repeat the experiment.

My Results Are:

Possible answer: Students should observe that the ball and the paperclip still reach the ground at the same time even though the paperclip is much lighter.

Name ______________________ Date ____________

Alternative Explore

Lesson 3

# Pendulum

## Materials

- string
- weights
- stand for making pendulum

## Procedure

1. Make a pendulum by hanging a weight from the string.
2. Start swinging the pendulum back and forth. Then let gravity take over.
3. Now count the number of swings there are in one minute.
4. Repeat the experiment using different weights. Measure the mass of each weight. Keep all factors the same for each experiment.
5. Record your results in the table.

| Weight | Number of swings per minute |
|---|---|
| #1 | |
| #2 | |
| #3 | |
| #4 | |

## Drawing Conclusions

How does mass affect the results?

The heavier weights have greater mass to move back and forth. Air resistance tends to have a greater effect on slowing objects with very little mass, so those with very little mass slow down faster. Disregarding air resistance for extremely light masses, the number of swings per minute should be the same regardless of the mass of the weight, so long as the length of the string is the same in each trial. The period of the pendulum depends on the length of the string, not on the mass or the weight.


Use with TE textbook page F33

Name ______________________ Date __________

Process Skill Builder
Lesson 3

# Use Numbers

## What Do I Weigh on Other Worlds?

The Sun, planets, and moons in the solar system have different masses and radii. This causes the force of gravity at their surfaces to vary from world to world (for a gaseous planet, the "surface" is the top of its atmosphere). As the mass of any world increases, surface gravity tends to be stronger. However, as the radius increases, surface gravity tends to weaken. How would your weight change from one world to the next?

Table 1 lists gravity multipliers for solar system bodies. These values show the combined effect of the objects' different masses and radii on surface gravity compared with Earth. You can use the gravity multipliers to find your weight on other worlds. Just multiply your weight on Earth by the gravity multiplier for the new world. On Neptune, for example, your weight would be your weight on Earth multiplied by 1.1.

**Table 1**

| Object | Gravity (Earth = 1) |
|---|---|
| Sun | 28 |
| Moon | 0.16 |
| Mars | 0.38 |
| Jupiter | 2.6 |
| Saturn | 1.07 |
| Neptune | 1.1 |
| Venus | 0.91 |
| Mercury | 0.38 |
| Uranus | 0.91 |

**Table 2**

| World | Weight of a 250-Pound Astronaut | Your weight in pounds |
|---|---|---|
| Sun | 7,000 lb | |
| Moon | 40 lb | |
| Mars | 95 lb | |
| Jupiter | 650 lb | |
| Saturn | 267.5 lb | |
| Neptune | 275 lb | |
| Venus | 227.5 lb | |
| Mercury | 95 lb | |
| Uranus | 227.5 lb | |

## Procedure

1. **Analyze** Study Tables 1 and 2. Look carefully to see how numbers were used in the examples in Table 2.
2. **Use Numbers** Complete Table 2.

Name ______________________ Date __________

**Process Skill Builder**

Lesson 3

## Drawing Conclusions

1. **Predict** A student who weighs 95 pounds on Earth has a mass of about 43 kg. What would the student's mass be on each world listed in Table 2?

   The student's mass on each planet would still be 43 kg. Mass does not vary with gravity.

2. **Infer** Saturn has much more mass than Earth, but your weight on Saturn is about the same as on Earth. How is this possible?

   Saturn is much less dense than Earth and its radius is much greater. A person on the surface of Saturn is far away from the center of Saturn, compared to Earth. Since gravity decreases with distance, the result is that the force of gravity is approximately the same for the two planets.

Name________________________ Date______________

Explore Activity
Lesson 4

# What Makes Sound?

**Hypothesize** What causes sound? Remember, sounds can be different. How could you build an instrument to test your ideas?

Write a **Hypothesis:**

Possible hypothesis: Students might hypothesize that sounds are produced by an object in motion.

**Materials**

- wood or plastic ruler
- long rubber band
- plastic or foam cup
- clear tape
- ballpoint pen
- scissors
- goggles

**Procedure** BE CAREFUL! Wear goggles.

1. Use a pen point to poke a hole in the bottom of the cup. Cut the rubber band. Insert one end into the hole. Tie two or three knots to keep the rubber band in place.
2. Tape the cup to the end of the ruler. Stretch the rubber band to the other end of the ruler. Tape it securely.
3. **Observe** Hold the cup next to your ear. Pluck the rubber band. Watch a partner do the same thing. Record what you hear and see.

   Students should hear a "twanging" sound. Pulling too hard results in a "snapping" sound of the band hitting the ruler.

4. **Experiment** Put one finger on the rubber band, hold it against the ruler, and then pluck it again. What happens to the sound?

   The rubber band sounds higher than in step 3.

Name ______________________ Date ____________

Explore Activity

Lesson 4

## Drawing Conclusions

1. **Infer** What did you observe that made your instrument work? How can you explain what makes sound?

   Something must move, or vibrate, to produce sound, such as plucking the rubber band.

2. What happened to the sound when you changed the rubber band with your finger? Explain why, based on your observations.

   The shorter the rubber band, the higher the sound. The longer the rubber band, the lower the sound. Students may predict that a shorter rubber band may vibrate faster.

3. **Going Further: Predict** What do you think will happen to the sound if you stretch the rubber band tighter? Untape the end of the rubber band and pull it a bit tighter. Retape the end to the ruler. Repeat steps 3 and 4. How do the results compare with your prediction? Give reasons for what happened.

   Students may predict that the sound will be higher.
   The tighter the rubber band, the higher the sound it produces.
   A tighter rubber band vibrates more quickly.

## Inquiry

Think of your own questions that you might like to test. What other factors might affect sound?

My Question Is:

Possible answer: What would happen to the sound if I filled the cup with cotton or paper?

How I Can Test It:

Possible answer: I can fill the cup with cotton or paper and conduct the experiment again.

My Results Are:

Possible answer: Plucking the rubber band produced a softer sound.

Name ______________________ Date ____________

Alternative Explore
Lesson 4

# Make a Drum

## Materials

- balloon
- scissors
- rubber bands
- sturdy 8-oz plastic bowl
- paper scraps

## Procedure

1. Cut a piece of the balloon large enough to stretch over the top of the bowl. Hint: Make a cut in the balloon from the hole to the top.
2. While your partner holds the balloon across the top of the bowl, use a rubber band to hold the balloon in place.
3. Tap the balloon with the eraser end of a pencil. Describe what you hear.

   Answers will vary.

4. Drop some paper scraps on the balloon. Repeat step 3. Describe what happens.

   The paper scraps should jump when the balloon is tapped.

5. Tap the balloon with different amounts of force. Describe what happens.

   Sound made will vary.

## Drawing Conclusions

1. What happens to the paper scraps when you tap the balloon "drum?" What does this tell you about what happens to the balloon "drum" when you tap it?

   The paper scraps bounce. It shows that the balloon is vibrating.

2. What happens when you change the force with which you tap the balloon "drum?" What does this tell you about the amount of energy in the balloon "drum?"

   The harder you tap, the more the paper scraps bounce. This shows that tapping harder gives the "drum" more energy.

3. Trace the flow of energy that begins when you tap the balloon.

   The energy goes from my hand to the pencil to the balloon to the paper and to the air.

Name ______________________ Date ____________

QUICK LAB
FOR SCHOOL OR HOME
Lesson 4

# Sound Carriers

**Hypothesize** Can sound travel through solids? Liquids?

Write a **Hypothesis:**

Possible hypothesis: Students might hypothesize that sounds can travel through solids and liquids.

## Materials

- sealable pint-sized plastic food bag filled with water
- wind-up clock
- wooden table or desk

## Procedure

1. **Observe** Put a wind-up clock on a wooden table. Put your ear against the table. Listen to the ticking. Lift your head. How well can you hear the ticking now? Record your observations.

   Students will not be able to hear the ticking as well after they lift their heads. Discuss that students are listening through the wood with the ear touching the table, but through air with the other ear.

2. **Use Variables** Fill a sealable pint-size plastic bag with water. Seal the bag. Hold it against your ear. Hold the clock against the bag. How well can you hear the ticking? Move your ear away from the bag. How well can you hear the ticking now?

   Students will not be able to hear the ticking as well after they move their ears away from the bag. Repeat the discussion for step 1, this time with the water-filled bag.

Name ______________________ Date ____________

QUICK LAB

FOR SCHOOL OR HOME

Lesson 4

## Drawing Conclusions

3. **Interpret Data** Rate wood, air, and water in order from best sound carrier to worst.

   Wood, water, air

4. **Experiment** How would you test other materials, like sand?

   Students may suggest they can fill a plastic bag with the materials to be tested and repeat step 2.

5. **Going Further** Think of your own questions that you might like to test. Do some solids carry sound better than others?

   My Question Is:

   Possible answer: Would a steel door or a wooden door be a better sound carrier?

   How I Can Test It:

   Possible answer: Students can stand on either side of a steel door and a wooden door and tap on the door.

   My Results Are:

   Students will hear a louder sound through the steel door.

Name ______________________ Date ____________

Explore Activity
Lesson 5

# How Can You Change a Sound?

**Hypothesize** Each musical instrument has a sound all its own. As you play an instrument, you make the sound change. What causes the sound to change? Test your hypothesis by building a homemade instrument from simple items like straws.

Write a **Hypothesis:**

Possible hypothesis: Students might hypothesize that sound changes because of the amount of air vibrating in an instrument.

## Materials

- 12 plastic drinking straws
- scissors
- metric ruler
- masking tape

### Procedure: Design Your Own

1. **Predict** Work in pairs to make a homemade instrument. Start with straws. Blow over one end of a straw. Will there be a difference if you seal the other end with tape? Record your prediction.

   Possible prediction: Taping one end of a straw makes it possible to produce a note.

2. **Observe** Tape one end and blow over the open end. Describe what you hear. Does it work better with or without one end taped?

   A vibrating air column inside the straw produces a note. Taping the end of the straw helps produce better notes.

3. **Classify** Repeat with different lengths cut from a straw. Try at least four lengths. How are the sounds different? Arrange the straws in order to hear the difference.

   Longer straws produce deeper sounds. Shorter straws produce higher sounds.

4. **Experiment** Flatten one end of a straw. Cut the end to a point. Wet it. With your lips stretched across your teeth, blow into that end of the straw. Try to make different sounds with the straw. How might you modify the instrument the girl is using in the photograph on page F55 in your textbook?

Name ______________________ Date __________

Explore Activity

Lesson 5

## Drawing Conclusions

1. **Infer** Why do you think the sounds changed when you cut different lengths of straw? Hint: What is inside the straw—even if it looks empty?

   The length of the column of air inside the straw changed.

2. **Communicate** Write a description of your instruments for a partner to build them exactly as you did. Include measurements taken with a ruler.

   Students should include measurements, such as the lengths of straws

3. **Going Further: Experiment** Try other materials to make other instruments. Try such things as bottles with water, craft sticks, and so forth. Tell what causes the sound to change in each case.

   Bottles with different amounts of water can be tapped or blown over. Different lengths of craft sticks can be extended over a desk edge and tapped.

**Inquiry**

Think of your own questions that you might like to test. What other factors affect the sound an instrument makes?

My Question Is:

Possible answer: Does the amount of water in a bottle affect the sound when I blow over its top?

How I Can Test It:

Possible answer: I can experiment with different amounts of water in a bottle.

My Results Are:

Possible answer: The more water in a bottle (the less air), the higher the pitch.

Name ______________________ Date __________

Alternative Explore
Lesson 5

# Make Some Music

## Procedure

1. Look at each of the instruments to see how it is played.
2. Play each of the instruments. Describe the sound each one makes.

Answers will vary depending on instruments.

3. Choose one of the instruments and investigate ways to change the volume (make the sound louder or softer). Record your results.
4. Investigate ways to change the instrument's pitch (make the sound higher or lower). Record your results.
5. Repeat steps 3 and 4 for each of the other instruments. Use another sheet of paper if you need to add to the table.

**Materials**

- simple wind instruments, such as recorder, mouth organ, slide whistle, or kazoo

| Instrument | How to Change Volume | How to Change Pitch |
|---|---|---|
| | | |
| | | |
| | | |
| | | |

## Drawing Conclusions

1. What changes the volume of wind instruments?

Blowing harder makes the volume louder. Blowing more softly makes the volume softer.

2. What changes the pitch of wind instruments?

Possible answer: Humming a different note on the kazoo, covering and uncovering holes in the recorder, and moving the slide in the slide whistle.

Name _________________________ Date ______________

**Process Skill Builder**
Lesson 5

# Communicate

## Making Tables and Graphs

In this activity you will interpret data, classify sounds, and create your own table. Tables are helpful tools that organize information. The table shown gives the loudness of some common sounds in decibels (dB). Sounds below 30 dB can barely be heard. Quiet sounds are between 30 dB and 50 dB. Moderate sounds begin at 50 dB. At 70 dB, sounds are considered noisy. At 110 dB and above, sounds are unbearable.

**LOUDNESS OF SOME SOUNDS**

| Sound | Loudness (in decibels) |
|---|---|
| Hearing limit | 0 |
| Rustling leaves | 10 |
| Whisper | 20 |
| Nighttime noises in house | 30 |
| Soft radio | 40 |
| Classroom/office | 50 |
| Normal conversation | 60 |
| Inside car on highway | 70 |
| Busy city street | 80 |
| Subway | 90 |
| Siren (30 meters away) | 100 |
| Thunder | 110 |
| **Pain threshold** | **120** |
| Loud indoor rock concert | 120 |
| Jet plane (30 meters away) | 140 |

## Procedure

1. **Classify** Determine which sounds are barely audible (can barely be heard), quiet, moderate, noisy, or unbearable.

   Barely audible (can barely be heard) Rustling leaves, whisper
   ______________________________________________

   Quiet Nighttime noises in house, soft radio
   ______________________________________________

Moderate Classroom/office, normal conversation

Noisy Inside car on highway, busy city street, subway, siren at 30 m
(may include thunder)

Unbearable Loud indoor rock concert, jet plane at 30 m
(may include thunder)

2. **Communicate** Make your own table to show how you classified the sounds. Use another sheet of paper if needed.
3. **Communicate** Make a data table to record how many quiet, moderate, noisy, or unbearable sounds you hear in one hour. Make a graph to show your results. "Number" is the vertical axis. "Kind of Sound" is the horizontal axis. Put the data table and graph on a separate sheet of paper.

## Drawing Conclusions

1. **Interpret Data** How much louder is a soft radio than your house at night? A classroom than a house at night?

   10 decibels, or 10 times, louder (10 X 1 = 10); 20 decibels, or
   100 times, louder (10 X 10 = 100)

2. **Interpret Data** How much softer is normal conversation than thunder?

   50 decibels, or 100,000 times, softer (10 X 10 X 10 X 10 X 10 = 100,000)

3. **Communicate** On another sheet of paper, make a chart listing loud sounds in their environment. What you can do to protect your ears from harm done by each loud noise?

   Possible answers: Lowering volume of loud radio; covering ears
   to protect against loud sounds.

Name ______________________ Date __________

Explore Activity
Lesson 6

# Do Sounds Bounce?

**Hypothesize** What happens when sound "hits" a surface? Does the kind of surface make a difference? Test your ideas.

Write a **Hypothesis:**

Possible hypothesis: Students might hypothesize that sound bounces off, passes through, or is absorbed by a particular surface.

## Materials

- 2 long cardboard tubes (can be taped, rolled-up newspapers)
- sound maker, such as a clicker or timer
- hard and soft test materials, such as a book, wood block, cloth, metal sheet, sponge, towel

### Procedure

1. Collect a variety of hard, smooth materials and soft, textured materials. Place one of the objects on a table. Set up your tubes in a V-shaped pattern on a table as shown in your textbook, page F65. The V should meet at the object you are testing. Record the name of the object in the first row of the table below.
2. **Observe** Place a sound maker (clicker or timer) at one end of the V. Listen for ticking at the other end of the V. Rank the loudness of the ticking on a scale of 1 (lowest) to 5 (highest). Record the number in the table.
3. **Experiment** Repeat steps 1 and 2 with the different materials you collected.

| Material/Object | Loudness Ranking |
|---|---|
| 1. | |
| 2. | |
| 3. | |
| 4. | |
| 5. | |

Name ______________________ Date ____________

Explore Activity
Lesson 6

## Drawing Conclusions

1. **Classify** What kinds of materials are the best reflectors—hard, smooth materials or soft, textured materials? What kinds of materials are the best absorbers?

   Best reflectors: hard, smooth materials; best absorbers: soft textured materials.

2. **Make a Model** Draw a diagram of the path of sound from the sound maker to your ear. On your diagram mark the point in the path where the sound wave bounced.

   Diagrams should show sound waves moving from the sound maker, through the first tube, going through or bouncing off the test material, then going through the second tube to the ear. Students should mark the test material at the point where the sound wave bounced.

3. **Going Further: Infer** Theaters often have soft velvet curtains, thick carpets, and cushioned seats. How do you think these objects affect the sound in a theater?

   These objects will absorb sound, making the theater quieter.

### Inquiry

Think of your own questions that you might like to test. What other materials are good reflectors and absorbers?

My Question Is:

Possible answer: What materials in my home are good reflectors and absorbers?

How I Can Test It:

Possible answer: I can set up my V-shaped experiment at home and test items around the house.

My Results Are:

Answers will vary. Best reflectors might include metal objects, such as a toaster; best absorbers might include soft materials, such as clothes.

Name ______________________ Date __________

Alternative Explore
Lesson 6

# Noisier or Quieter?

**Materials**

- 2 paper or plastic cups
- string
- tape
- tissues

## Procedure

1. Work with a partner. Poke a hole in the bottom of each cup.
2. Thread a piece of string through each hole so that one end of the string is inside each cup. Knot the string and tape each end to the bottom of the cup.
3. You and your partner hold the cups so that the string is pulled tight. While you hold one cup to your ear, have your partner speak into the other cup, using a normal tone of voice. Describe what you hear.

   Students will be able to hear their partners talking.

4. Switch roles with your partner, so that your partner has a chance to hear, too.
5. Put some tissues in the your cup. Then repeat step 3. Describe what you hear.

   The partners' voices will be softer.

6. Switch roles with your partner, so that your partner has a chance to hear, too.

## Drawing Conclusions

1. When was the sound you heard quieter, with or without the tissues?

   With the tissues

2. Explain why there was a difference.

   Possible answer: The tissues absorbed some of the sound energy, so less sound reached the listener's ear.

Name ______________________ Date ____________

QUICK LAB

FOR SCHOOL OR HOME

Lesson 6

# Clap! Clap!

**Hypothesize** Can you cause a clear time lag between a sound and its echo? Write a **Hypothesis:**

Possible hypothesis: Students might hypothesize that they can set up an experiment to time the lag between a sound and its echo.

## Materials

- meterstick

## Procedure

1. **Observe** Stand about 8 m away from a large wall, such as the side of your school building. Make sure there is plenty of open space between you and the wall. Clap your hands, and listen for an echo. Notice how much time there is between your clap and the echo.

   Have students use a stopwatch to time the interval between the clap and the echo.

2. **Observe** Move closer to the wall, and clap again. Listen for an echo. Try this several times.

   Answers will vary, but the time recorded will be less than in step 1.Have students take turns, using the meterstick to measure their distance from the wall.

Name ______________________ Date ____________

QUICK LAB
FOR SCHOOL OR HOME
Lesson 6

## Drawing Conclusions

3. **Observe** As you got closer to the wall, how did the time between the clap and the echo change? Did you always hear an echo? Explain.

   As students get closer to the wall, the time between the clap and the echo decreases. They will not always hear an echo. The time interval between the clap and the echo may be too small to be measured.

4. **Experiment** Repeat at different distances. What happens?

   Suggest students try increasing the distance from the starting position and observe what happens. The farther the distance, the longer it takes to hear the echo.

5. **Going Further** Think of your own questions that you might like to test. Will you get the same results if you try other sounds?

   My Question Is:

   Possible answer: Will a louder sound give the same results?

   How I Can Test It:

   Possible answer: Repeat the same steps and conditions with other short, loud sounds, such as slamming a book, clapping bricks together, or beating a drum.

   My Results Are:

   The difference in loudness, or pitch, does not affect the results since sounds travel through air at the same speed.

Name _______________ Date _______________

Explore Activity

Lesson 7

# Can You See Without Light?

**Hypothesize** Is it possible to see objects if there is no light? Test your ideas.

Write a **Hypothesis:**

Possible hypothesis: Students might hypothesize that it is not possible to see an object if there is no light.

**Materials**

- small cardboard box with lid
- small object to put inside box, such as an eraser, crayon, or coin
- scissors
- flashlight

## Procedure

**BE CAREFUL!** Handle scissors carefully. Do not put any sharp objects in the box.

1. Cut a hole about the size of a dime in the box as shown. Put an object inside the box. Close the lid.
2. **Observe** Look in the box through the hole. What do you see? Write a description of it.

   Students should not be able to see anything.
3. Now cut a small hole in the top of the box.
4. **Experiment** Shine the flashlight through the top hole while you look into the box again. Can you see the object this time?

   The object in the box should now be visible.

## Drawing Conclusions

1. **Communicate** Could you see the object inside the box in step 2? In step 4? Explain any difference in your answers.

   The object is not visible in step 2 because there is no light to bounce off the object. It is visible in step 4 because light bounces off the object and reaches the eye.
2. **Infer** Is it possible to see an object in the dark? Explain.

   Students should infer that it is not possible to see an object in the dark because light is necessary for the object to be visible.

**3. Predict** Do any characteristics of the object in the box affect the results? Try different kinds of objects. Predict any differences in your results. Test your ideas.

Objects with light colors might be more visible in the box, especially if the interior of the box is black. It could be tested by placing objects, identical in every way but color, into the box and noting any difference in visibility.

**4. Going Further: Predict** How much extra lighting would you need on a dark, cloudy day in order to safely walk around your classroom or your room at home? Would a night-light work? How would you test your ideas safely?

Students might respond that neither a night-light nor a single light bulb would provide enough light, but that overhead classroom lights would. Students should not walk while they test their ideas, but should stand still and observe the floor, walls, and large objects for visibility.

## Inquiry

Think of your own questions that you might like to test. What other factors about objects in the box might make them visible?

My Question Is:

Possible answer: Could I see a shiny object in the box without using a flashlight?

How I Can Test It:

I can repeat the experiment with a shiny object.

My Results Are:

I cannot see the object without light.

Name ______________________ Date __________

Alternative Explore
Lesson 7

# Can You See the Flashlight?

**Procedure** **BE CAREFUL!** Handle scissors carefully.

**Materials**
- scissors
- flashlight
- small cardboard box with lid, such as a shoebox

1. Cut a small hole in the end of a cardboard box. Place the flashlight inside the box. Do not turn on the flashlight.
2. Discuss with your group whether you can see the flashlight if you look through the hole.
3. Try it. Can you see the flashlight?

   Students should not be able to see the flashlight.
4. What could you do to be able to see the flashlight inside the box? Make a list of your group's suggestions.

   Groups may suggest turning on the flashlight or cutting another hole in the box.
5. Test your ideas. Record your observations.

   Results will vary depending on ideas tested.

## Drawing Conclusions

1. What ideas did your group test? Did they make it possible for you to see the flashlight?

   Answers will vary. Students will likely try turning on the flashlight or cutting another hole in the box. Both of these ideas will work.
2. What do your results tell you is necessary for you to be able to see something?

   There must be a source of light.

Name ____________________ Date __________

QUICK LAB

FOR SCHOOL OR HOME

Lesson 7

# Follow the Bouncing Light

**Hypothesize** How does light travel when it bounces off a mirror? Write a **Hypothesis:**

Possible hypothesis: Students might hypothesize that light bouncing off a mirror travels in straight lines at equal angles.

## Materials

- mirror
- string

## Procedure

1. Hold a small pocket mirror as shown. Adjust it so your partner can see your face in the middle of the mirror.

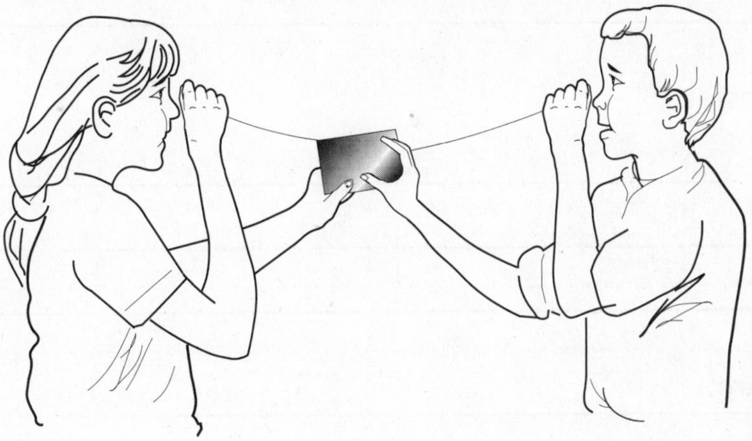

2. Have your partner run a piece of string from the tip of his or her nose to the reflection of your nose in the mirror. Leave a length of string dangling at the mirror. Then run the extra string from the mirror to the tip of your nose. Be sure the string is taut. Note the angles formed between the string and the mirror.
3. **Observe** Move a little farther apart. How does the mirror have to be moved in order for your partner to see your face?

Students should note that the mirror must be kept midway between them.

Name ______________________ Date __________

QUICK LAB
FOR SCHOOL OR HOME
Lesson 7

## Drawing Conclusions

4. **Interpret Data** Were both of you able to see each other in the mirror? What did you observe about the angles the string made with the mirror?

   Yes, we could see each other. The angles seem to be about the same size.

5. **Going Further** Think of your own questions that you might like to test. Will light bounce off objects other than mirrors?

   My Question Is:

   Will light bounce off other objects with a shiny surface?

   How I Can Test It:

   Possible answer: Students can repeat the experiment with shiny objects such as a large spoon or metal dish.

   My Results Are:

   Results will vary depending on objects tested. A clean, shiny, reflective surface should produce a clear image.

Name ______________________ Date ____________

**Explore Activity**
Lesson 8

# What Can Light Pass Through?

**Hypothesize** How do objects cast shadows? Do all objects cast shadows the same way? Are all shadows alike? How would you test your ideas?

Write a **Hypothesis:**

Possible hypothesis: Students might hypothesize that objects cast shadows when light cannot pass through them; objects let differing amounts of light through, thus casting different shadows.

## Materials

- plastic sandwich bag
- paper
- waxed paper
- aluminum foil
- other assorted materials to test
- flashlight
- clear-plastic cup
- water (other liquids, optional)
- food dye

## Procedure

1. **Classify** Sort the test materials into those that you think light can pass through and those that light cannot pass through.
2. **Experiment** Use the flashlight to test if light can pass through each of the solid materials. Record your observations. Test if light will pass through water. What about water colored with food dye?

   Students should find that light passes through the plastic bag and clear plastic cup; some light passes through waxed paper and paper; no light passes through aluminum foil; light passes through colored and uncolored water.
3. **Infer** How can you test if light passes through gases? Explain. What materials would you need?

   Air is a gas and light passes through air. To conduct an experiment, you need a light source.

## Drawing Conclusions

1. **Interpret Data** Can light pass through all the materials equally well?

   No. It didn't pass well through waxed paper.

2. **Interpret Data** Can light pass through solids, liquids, and gases?

Yes, light passes through some, but not all solids; water, which is a liquid; and air, which is a gas.

3. **Predict** What else might you add to water to see if light gets through—sand, ink, instant coffee? Predict if each lets light through. How would you test your ideas?

Students might suggest other substances such as flour or different colors of food dye. They might test their predictions by adding the ingredients to water and following the procedures.

4. **Going Further: Experiment** Design a room from window coverings to lighting, where shadows of objects are always soft and fuzzy, never sharp. What sorts of materials would you use?

Answers will vary, but should reflect an understanding that objects that let some light through cast softer, fuzzier shadows than objects that don't let any light through.

## Inquiry

Think of your own questions that you might like to test. What other factors affect shadows?

My Question Is:

Possible answer: How does the brightness of light affect the clarity of shadows?

How I Can Test It:

Possible answer: I can experiment with bright and dim lights to compare and contrast the shadows they make.

My Results Are:

Possible answer: Bright light casts harsher, sharper shadows than dim light.

Name ______________________ Date ____________

Alternative Explore

Lesson 8

# Rank Shadows

**Materials**

- plastic sandwich bag
- aluminum foil
- waxed paper
- flashlight
- clear-plastic cup
- water
- food dye
- other materials to test
- paper

## Procedure

1. Sort through the materials your teacher gives you to work with. Predict which will make the sharpest shadows. Record your predictions.

   Students might predict that objects they cannot see through will make the sharpest shadows.

2. With the room somewhat darkened, shine a flashlight on each item to be tested. Try to make a shadow on a wall. Notice how sharp each shadow is. Record your observations.

   Observations will vary depending on objects tested.

## Drawing Conclusions

1. Rank the materials in terms of the shadows they produce, from the sharpest shadow to the least sharp.

   Answers will vary, depending on the materials available. Opaque objects will make the sharpest shadows. Translucent objects will make less sharp shadows. Transparent objects will make very indistinct, difficult-to-see shadows.

2. What pattern can you see in the kinds of materials you tested and the shadows they made?

   The less you can see through an object the more distinct the shadow will be.

Name ______________________ Date ____________

QUICK LAB

FOR SCHOOL OR HOME

Lesson 8

# Seeing Through a Lens

**Hypothesize** What happens when you view the room through a lens? How does it change the way things look? Write a **Hypothesis:**

Possible hypothesis: Students might hypothesize that lenses make things look bigger or smaller.

## Materials

- convex lens (magnifying glass)
- index card or piece of paper

## Procedure

1. **Observe** Hold a convex lens about a foot from your eye. View the image of the room around you. Record what you see. Repeat with the lens quite close to the page of a book.

   Students should see an inverted, reduced view of the room using a typical short-focus magnifying glass.

   Make sure students hold the lens within an inch or two of the book so it will produce an enlarged, upright image.

2. **Experiment** Aim the lens at a light bulb or window. Move an index card back and forth on the other side of the lens until you see an image of the light source cast sharply on the card. Record what you see.

   An inverted, reduced image will be cast on the card when the window or light bulb is well removed from the lens.

Name ______________________ Date ____________

QUICK LAB
FOR SCHOOL OR HOME
Lesson 8

## Drawing Conclusions

3. **Observe** When the image was upright, was it enlarged or reduced?

   Enlarged

4. **Observe** When you cast an image on the card, was it upright or inverted?

   Inverted

5. **Classify** Summarize your observations in a table on a separate sheet of paper.

   Results will vary depending on the focal length of the lens used.

6. **Going Further** Think of your own questions that you might like to test. Does the distance of the object from the lens affect the image?

   My Question Is:

   Possible answer: What will happen if I move the lens away from the book?

   How I Can Test It:

   Possible answer: Observe the book page through the lens while slowly moving the lens away from the book.

   My Results Are:

   The image becomes smaller as I move the lens away.

Name ____________________ Date ____________

Explore Activity
Lesson 9

# What Is Color?

**Hypothesize** What color will a blue object appear to be if you look at it under a blue light? Under a red light? How could you test your ideas even if you did not have a red or blue light bulb?

Write a **Hypothesis:**

Possible hypothesis: Students might hypothesize that a blue object would appear blue under blue light and grayish under red light.

## Materials

- red, yellow, blue, and green cellophane sheets
- white paper
- crayons
- red, yellow, blue, green, and black squares of construction paper
- flashlight

## Procedure

1. **Observe** Instead of using colored light bulbs, shine a flashlight at a sheet of white paper through each of the cellophane sheets. Record what you see.

   Students will note that the color visible on white paper is the same as the color of the filter.

2. **Predict** Is there a difference if you observe the paper by looking through colored cellophane instead? What color will each of the colored squares appear to be through each of the cellophane sheets? Check your predictions.

   Students might predict that the colored squares will appear to be the same color as the cellophane sheet they are viewed through. Students will find that each colored square absorbs all colors but its own, and each color of cellophane allows only its own color to pass through.

3. **Make a Model** Use the crayons to make additional colored squares to view through the cellophane sheets.

4. **Communicate** Make a table on a separate sheet of paper that shows what color each square appears to be through each of the cellophane sheets.

## Drawing Conclusions

1. **Communicate** What color does the red square appear to be when viewed through the red cellophane sheet? Why? What color does the blue square appear to be when viewed through the red cellophane sheet? Why?

   The red square appears red because a red object reflects red light and the red cellophane only lets red light through. The blue square appears dark gray or black because a blue object reflects blue light, but the red cellophane only lets red light through.

2. **Going Further: Predict** What do you think would happen if you looked at the red square through both the red and blue cellophane sheets at the same time? Try it to test your prediction.

   Students might predict the square will appear black. The red square reflects red light, which will pass through the red cellophane. However, the red light will be absorbed by the blue cellophane, making the square look black.

**Inquiry**

Think of your own questions that you might like to test. How does mixing colors of light differ from other ways to mix colors?

My Question Is:

Possible answer: How does mixing food dye differ from mixing light?

How I Can Test It:

Possible answer: I can experiment with food dye to compare and contrast my results with mixing light.

My Results Are:

Possible answer: Mixing colors of food dye creates different colors than mixing colors of light.

Name ______________________ Date ____________

Alternative Explore
Lesson 9

# What Is Color?

**Materials**

- shoe box with lid
- scissors
- red cellophane
- tape
- small white object
- small red object
- small green object
- flashlight

**Procedure** BE CAREFUL! Handle scissors carefully.

1. Cut a rectangle from the lid of the box. Tape red cellophane over the hole.
2. Cut a small viewing hole in the side of the box.
3. Place a small white object in the box. Replace the lid.
4. Shine a flashlight through the cellophane. Look at the object through the viewing hole. What color does the object appear to be?

   Red

5. Remove the white object and place a red object and a green object in the box. Replace the lid.
6. Shine a flashlight through the cellophane. Look at the objects through the viewing hole. What color does each object appear to be?

   The red object appears red, and the green object appears a dark color.

## Drawing Conclusions

1. What color did the white object look inside the box? Red
2. What color did the red object look inside the box? Red
3. What color did the green object look inside the box?

   Possible answers: dark gray, dark brown, or black

4. Explain your results.

   Red light passes through the red cellophane and strikes the objects. The white object reflects all colors of light, so it reflects the red light. The red object reflects red light, so it looks red. The green object does not reflect red light, so it looks dark. Accept all reasonable responses.

Name ______________________ Date __________

Process Skill Builder

Lesson 9

# Predict

## Mixing Colors

You will use pigments–colored substances–in this activity to see the way pigments blend to make the other colors.

In this activity you will make a prediction before you do the activity. That is, you will make a reasonable guess about what you expect the results to be. Predict what colors will result when you mix certain colors of food dyes together.

**Materials**

- red, yellow, blue and green food dyes
- water
- plastic cups
- goggles

**Procedure** BE CAREFUL! Wear goggles.

1. Place four cups on a piece of paper. Add enough water to each cup to cover the bottom.
2. **Predict** What color will be made by mixing one drop of red food dye and one drop of yellow food dye in the water? Mix well. Record the result.

| | |
|---|---|
| Prediction | |
| Results | Mixing red and yellow produces the color orange. |

3. **Experiment** Do step 2 with red and blue dyes. Be sure to make a prediction before you mix the colors.

| | |
|---|---|
| Prediction | |
| Results | Mixing red and blue produces the color purple. |

4. **Experiment** Do step 2 again with yellow and blue, and then with all four colors. Again, be sure to make your predictions before you mix the colors.

| | |
|---|---|
| Prediction | |
| Results | Mixing yellow and blue produces green. |

| | |
|---|---|
| Prediction | |
| Results | Mixing all four colors produces black. |

### Drawing Conclusions

1. **Communicate** What color resulted when you mixed red and yellow?

Orange; mixing two colors produces a third color.

2. **Communicate** What color resulted when you mixed red and blue? Blue and yellow? When you mixed all four colors?

Purple; green; black

3. **Infer** What would happen if you used different amounts of each dye? Experiment to find out. Make predictions about the final color before you mix the dyes.

Results will depend on colors and amounts students mix.

| Color/Amount | Prediction | Results |
|---|---|---|
| | | |
| | | |
| | | |
| | | |

Name ______________________ Date ____________

Explore Activity
Lesson 10

# How Do Waves Move?

**Hypothesize** How can you make waves move faster or slower? Test your ideas.

Write a **Hypothesis:**

Possible hypothesis: Students might hypothesize that waves can be made to move faster or slower by changing the matter they travel through or changing the origin of the wave.

## Materials

- two 1-m strips of tape
- 20 straws
- meterstick
- 20 paper clips
- stopwatch or digital watch

## Procedure

1. Work in groups of four. Starting 10 cm from one end, press 20 straws onto the sticky surface of a strip of tape. Be sure the straws are 4 cm apart, centered, and parallel. Secure them with the second strip.
2. **Observe** Have two members of your group each take one end of the model, so it spreads out lengthwise. Have a third person tap a straw at one end. Have the fourth person time how long the wave takes to travel across from one end of the model to the other. Record the time it takes.

   Answers will vary depending on the strength of the tap.

3. **Experiment** Repeat step 2 several times, sometimes with the model tightly stretched, other times with it loosely stretched. Record your results in the table below. The waves will travel faster with the model tightly stretched.

| Description of Model | Time |
|---|---|
| | |
| | |
| | |
| | |

Name ______________________ Date ______________

Explore Activity
Lesson 10

## Drawing Conclusions

1. **Observe** In what direction does the wave move? In what direction do the straws move?

   As the straws move up and down, the wave moves horizontally from where the straw was tapped to the other end of the tape.

2. **Interpret Data** How does holding it tighter or looser change how the wave moves?

   Students should note that when the model is stretched tightly, the wave moves faster; when the model is stretched loosely, the wave moves more slowly.

3. **Going Further: Experiment** Place paper clips at the ends of the first ten straws. Repeat steps 2 and 3 of the procedure. What happens? Try other combinations of paper clips. What happens? Record your results in the table below.

   Students might find that adding paper clips (matter) causes the wave to travel more slowly.

| Paper-Clip Combination | Results |
|---|---|
| | |
| | |
| | |

**Inquiry**

Think of your own questions that you might like to test. Does the strength of the force affect the motion of a wave?

My Question Is:

Possible answer: Will the wave travel faster if I tap the model harder?

How I Can Test It:

Possible answer: I can repeat step 2 several times, tapping the model with increasingly greater force.

My Results Are:

Possible answer: The greater the force, the faster the wave moves.

Name ______________________ Date ____________

Alternative Explore

Lesson 10

# Change of Speed

## Procedure

**Materials**

- jump rope
- thinner rope

1. Work in a group. Two students will hold the ends of the rope. A third student will be the counter. A fourth student will be the recorder.
2. The students holding the rope should hold it taut. One student starts a single vertical vibration at one end while the counter begins to count seconds or keep time on a watch with a second hand. The counter should stop as soon as the vibration reaches the other end of the rope.
3. Record the time it took for the wave to travel the length of the rope.

   Answers will vary.
4. Group members should change jobs and repeat the experiment.
5. Repeat the experiment with the thinner rope. Record the time it took for the wave to travel the length of the rope.

   Answers will vary.
6. Try varying the height of the vibration on each rope. Does this change the time it takes for the wave to move along the rope?

   No

## Drawing Conclusions

1. On which rope did the wave move more quickly?

   The thinner rope
2. Did the height of the vibration that moved down the rope affect the speed?

   No
3. What determines the speed at which a wave travels?

   The medium, or material through which it passes

Name ______________________ Date ____________

QUICK LAB
FOR SCHOOL OR HOME
Lesson 10

# Water Waves

**Hypothesize** How do water waves affect the motion of floating objects? Test your ideas. Write your **Hypothesis:**

Possible hypothesis: Students might hypothesize that floating objects move up and down on water waves.

## Materials

- aluminum foil
- shallow pan at least 20 x 28 cm
- water
- pencil

## Procedure

1. Fill a shallow pan or tray (20 by 28 cm) half full of water. Fold small squares of foil (1 cm by 1 cm) into tiny "boats." Place several of these boats on the surface of the water.
2. At one end of the tray, make waves on the water's surface. Do this by moving your pencil horizontally up and down in the water.
3. **Predict** What do you think will happen to the boats after 30 seconds? After one minute? Record your predictions.

   Students might predict that their boats will move across the tray, moving farther after one minute than after 30 seconds.